D0649948

# THE AUDUBON
# NATURE
# ENCYCLOPEDIA

# THE AUDUBON
# NATURE
# ENCYCLOPEDIA

SPONSORED BY THE NATIONAL AUDUBON SOCIETY

## VOLUME 10

SE-TE

CURTIS BOOKS
*A division of*
The Curtis Publishing Company
Philadelphia — New York

CREATED AND PRODUCED BY
COPYLAB PUBLISHING COUNSEL, INC., NEW YORK

Published simultaneously in Canada by
Curtis Distributing Company, Ltd., Toronto.




Printed in the United States of America

PICTORIAL ACKNOWLEDGEMENTS, Volume 10

Michael H. Bevans, VIII, 1930, 1933, 1979 —Woodbridge Williams, 1794, 1975 (both courtesy of the National Park Service) —Peter A. Thomas*, 1799 —Alfred M. Bailey*, 1801 —W. D. Berry, 1802, 1831, 1934, 1935, 1936, 1938 —National Park Service, 1804 —Lena Scott Harris, 1805, 1866 right —Allan D. Cruickshank*, 1810, 1812, 1823, 1826, 1844 top, 1890, 1893, 1901, 1904, 1921, 1922-23, 1939, 1941, 1957, 1959, 1962, 1963, 1964, 1965, 1983 —Allan Brooks, 1811, 1865, 1881, 1892, 1895, 1896, 1899, 1943, 1960, 1986 —John K. Terres, 1813, 1815, 1816-17, 1818, 1819, 1844 bottom, 1928, 1949 —Audubon's Elephant Folio, 1821, 1903, 1974, 1984 —A. Starkey, 1824, 1852 —Jack Dermid*, 1827 —Woodrow Goodpaster*, 1828 —Louis Agassiz Fuertes, 1829 (courtesy of the Massachusetts Department of Agriculture) —Arthur W. Ambler*, 1832, 1987 —Karl Weidmann*, 1835, 1836 —Anthony D'Attilio, 1840-41 —N. E. Beck, Jr.*, 1843 —Stephen Dalton*, 1849 —Isabelle H. Conant, 1850, 1851, 1857 —Wayne Trimm, 1854-55 (courtesy of the New York State Conservationist), 1912-13 (courtesy of The New York State Conservationist) —John H. Gerard*, 1858 top, 1806-07, 1980 —Karl H. Maslowski*, 1858 bottom, 1985 —Don Wooldridge*, 1861 —Walter Sibley, 1862 —G. Ronald Austing*, 1864 top, 1861 —Tom McHugh*, 1864 bottom —Gaston LePage*, 1866 left —American Museum of Natural History, 1867, 1869 left, 1870 —C. C. Nikiforoff, 1869 right (courtesy of the Geographical Review) —United States Department of Agriculture, 1871, 1946 — Dawson*, 1878 — Lee Adams, 1880, 1926, 1947 — C.J. Henry, 1882, 1883, 1884-5 middle, 1885 right, 1887 —Charles J. Ott*, 1884 left —Roger Tory Peterson, 1898 —R. Bruce Horsfall, 1900, 1945 —Bucky Reeves*, 1906 —Walter Van Riper, 1909, 1910, 1914 (all courtesy of the Colorado Museum of Natural History) —Lynwood M. Chace*, 1916, 1917, 1918 —H. W. Kitchen*, 1920 —Helen Cruickshank*, 1953 —The New York State Conservationist, 1955 —Hugh M. Halliday*, 1958 —George Porter*, 1967, 1981 —Gordon S. Smith*, 1971, 1988 —A. U. Hull, 1972 (courtesy of the United States Fish and Wildlife Service) —Winston E. Banko, 1973 —Edmund J. Sawyer, 1976 —Leonard Lee Rue*, III, 1978 —Bernard Gluck*, 1992

*Photographs from Photo-Film Department of National Audubon Society

*Sequoia trees attain the greatest bulk, though not height, in the plant kingdom*

# SEQUOIA

**Other Common Names** — Sierra redwood, giant sequoia, big-tree

**Scientific Name** — *Sequoiadendron giganteum*

**Family** — Taxodiaceae (taxodium family)

**Range** — In separate groves on the western slopes of the Sierra Nevada in California, between 5,000 and 8,000 feet elevation

**Habitat** — Occurs in the clear air of mountains where much of its moisture comes from deep winter snows

**Leaves** — Pointed overlapping scales one-eighth to one-half inch long of rather dull green, growing along the twigs like a cedar

**Bark** — Up to two feet thick and reddish brown, usually lighter and more tan than the redwood, with deep vertical cracks or grooves

**Flower** — Tiny blossoms on the tips of the foliage in February or March, producing much pollen

**Fruit** — Oval cones much like the redwood but with more scales and larger, two to three inches long. They mature the second year but may remain closed and on the tree for 20 years

The Sequoia, or Sierra redwood, *Sequoiadendron giganteum*, is confined to California alone, and is limited there to the western slope of the Sierra Nevada, with an interrupted longitudinal range of 250 miles. The 76 groves grow at altitudes varying from 4,500 to 8,000 feet and cover a total area of some 35,600 acres. The northernmost grove consists of a group of six trees, hidden in a forest of pines and firs near the southern border of Placer County. At the southern limit are the 23 fine groves of the Sequoia National Forest, Tulare County.

Between the several northern groves gaps of from 40 to 60 miles exist, while in the southern part of the range the broad belt of Sequoias is broken only by deep river-cut canyons. The gaps between the northern groves correspond with the beds of glaciers that flowed from the main high crests of the Sierra Nevada during the Pleistocene Epoch.

Sequoias grow where the snow lies deep in winter and the temperature may drop to zero for short periods, while in summer humidity is low and the temperature is high, save when the rare thunderstorms bring brief showers. Usually the trees occupy sheltered valleys lying between low ridges, where deep humus conserves the winter moisture.

Sub-surface water is necessary to both the Sequoia and the redwood for they lack tap-roots, and the widely radiating root systems do not penetrate deeply into the ground. When the Sequoias were discovered many reports credited them with ages varying from 3,000 to 5,000 years. More conservative estimates have come with the cutting of the trees and the counting of growth rings. Mature trees are now considered to be from 400 to 1,500 years of age, with only a few giants attaining more than 2,000 years. John Muir, however, believed that one exceedingly large tree that he examined showed an age of 4,000 years.

Largest in bulk of the Sequoias is the *"General Sherman Tree,"* growing in a forest of 5,000 trees on the Marble Fork of the Kaweah River in Sequoia National Park. This tree has a height of 272 feet. The trunk is 103 feet in circumference at the swollen base. Twelve feet above the ground it is 82 feet and 4 inches in circumference. A tree in the North Calaveras Grove has been found to measure 325 feet in height, tallest of the Sequoias.

Both the redwood and the Sequoia are very fire resistant, because of the asbestoslike quality of the thick, fibrous bark and its high tannin content. Many of the older trees, however, are fire-hollowed where flames gained entrance to the heartwood at the base of the trunk during repeated forest fires, perhaps centuries ago. Old logs are sometimes found on the forest floor so hol-

*The trunk of the Sequoia is a fluted buttressed column rising more than 250 feet*

lowed by fire that little is left save the resistant bark. One such prostrate trunk in the North Calaveras Grove has been so tunneled by fire that a horseman can ride through its entire length.

A typical grove of Sequoias such as the North Calaveras Grove, is more open than is one of the coast redwoods, allowing incense cedars, white fir, sugar and yellow pines, and black oaks to grow up among the dominant trees. Dogwoods, azaleas, and California yews grow along the little stream in the grove.

Some of the earliest national parks were created in an effort to save the Sequoias. Yosemite, Sequoia, and General Grant National Parks were established in 1890 through the efforts of

*Majestic mountains and giant Sequoias are abundant at Sequoia National Park*

early conservationists. Both Yosemite and Sequoia National Park were created primarily for the preservation of the Sequoias. In 1940 General Grant National Park became part of a larger reserve, Kings Canyon National Park. In 1954 a large tract—South Calaveras Grove—was purchased near North Calaveras Grove. The Calaveras Parkway, designed to connect the two groves will make the South Grove accessible to the public. At present, over 90 percent of the Sequoias are in national parks or forests. (*See also Redwood*)

## SEQUOIA NATIONAL PARK
**Location**—Central California
**Size**—604 square miles
**Mammals**—Bighorn sheep, mule deer, black bears, raccoons, ringtails, marmots, squirrels, mountain beavers, opossums, foxes, coyotes, pikas
**Birdlife**—Eagles, hawks, grouse, Steller's jays, water ouzels, many others
**Plants**—Sequoias, firs, incense cedars, ponderosa and sugar pines, many hardwoods

The giant sequoias, some of which are 3,500 years old, are among the largest living species in the world. Slightly smaller in height, they are more massive than the coastal redwoods, measuring up to 36 feet in diameter at the base (*See also Redwood*).

The park, on the western slope of the Sierra Nevada, includes Mount Whitney —14,494 feet high—the tallest mountain in the United States, excluding Alaska.

Kings Canyon National Park, adjoining Sequoia on the north, contains 710 square miles of similar terrain, and also some redwood forests.
**Accommodations**—At Giant Forest Lodge and campgrounds
**Headquarters**—Three Rivers, California

## SHAD
**American Shad**
**Other Common Names**—None
**Scientific Name** — *Alosa sapidissima*
**Family**—Clupeidae (herrings)
**Order**—Clupeiformes
**Size**—Length, about 2½ feet
**Range**—Along Atlantic Coast of North America from the Gulf of St. Lawrence to the St. Johns River in Florida

The American shad has a deep body with a sharp, rather than rounded, horizontal belly line. Its upper jaw reaches to below the rear margin of the eye. Young specimens have small teeth in the upper jaw but lose them as they mature.

*The American shad occasionally weighs as much as 13 pounds*

Both the dorsal fin and the anal fin are of moderate size and are not spiny. The tail fin is deeply forked (*See Topography of a Fish, under Fish*).

The fish's back and upper sides are dark blue or green. The lower sides and belly are white and silvery. A dark spot is just behind the gill and is followed by one or two horizontal rows of smaller spots.

The American shad leaves the ocean at spawning time. It swims up rivers to spawn in either brackish or fresh water. Its chief food is the small, floating forms of life collectively known as plankton. —M.R.

## SHARK

Although everyone knows something about sharks, few realize how many different kinds there are. Just a few families of sharks, each containing several or many different species, are Lamnidae (mackerel sharks); Scyliorhinidae (cat sharks); Carcharhinidae (requiem sharks); Sphyrnidae (hammerhead sharks); Squalidae (dogfish sharks). One shark, however, the maneater, is best known and is considered by most to be the most fearsome.

**Maneater Shark**
**Other Common Names**—White shark
**Scientific Name**—*Carcharadon carcharias*
**Family**—Lamnidae (mackerel sharks)

**Order**—Squaliformes
**Size**—Length, about 20 feet. One specimen recorded at 36½ feet
**Range**—Not numerous anywhere but found throughout the world in tropical, subtropical, and warmer ocean waters of the temperate zone. Stragglers are found as far north as Newfoundland

The maneater shark has a strong, torpedo-shaped body which leads smoothly into its large head (25 to 30 percent of the length of the fish) and pointed snout. On each side of the head are five long gill openings. The front dorsal fin forms an almost perfect equilateral triangle but its apex is rounded and its rear margin is slightly concave. The rear dorsal fin is only about one-sixth the size of the front dorsal. The pectoral fins are large and sickle-shaped. The tail fin is lunately-shaped with the upper portion slightly longer than the lower and deeply notched toward its tip. The fish's teeth are large, strong, sharp, and serrated on their edges.

Maneaters are dully colored: dark on top, lighter on bottom. They prey on a wide variety of fishes and other sea animals. They are also known to attack and kill human beings and are the only sharks which have been proven to attack small boats. (*See also under Fish: Some Common Marine Fishes of the North Atlantic Coast*) —M.R.

# SHARKS, RAYS, AND CHIMERAS

The wholly marine members of the phylum Chordata, those animals with backbones that breathe water through gills, are called fishes. The three classes of fishes are the jawless fishes, the bony fishes, and the class Chondrichthyes that includes the sharks, rays, and chimeras (*See under Fish*).

All of the Chondrichthyes have skeletons of cartilage, a white, tough, elastic substance that is also known as gristle. In mammals, birds, and true fishes, the bones (except in the skull) are formed of cartilage that gradually turns to bone as growth slows and stops; in the chondrichthyes, or cartilaginous fishes, bone does not develop.

Other characteristics differentiate sharks and their kindred from the true, or bony, fishes. The scales, in this class, are denticles, or placoid scales, each composed of dentine coated with enamel, practically the same as teeth. Where true fishes usually have one gill slit on each side, sharks and their allies have from four to seven pairs, and often have another pair of openings behind the eye called spiracles. The mouth, in this class, is on the underside of the body.

## Sharks

Sharks are cylindrical in shape, tapering at both ends, and adapted for rapid movement. Rays and skates are flattened, though some, such as the formidably armed sawfish (*see Sawfish*), are nearly sharklike in form, but have the gill slits underneath the body instead of on the sides as sharks do. The chimeras, or ratfishes, have the underslung mouth, placoid scales, and four gill slits beneath a single cover, but a fishlike form.

Sharks are placed in three orders— Diplospondyli (notidanoid sharks), Asterospondyli (true sharks), and Cyclospondyli (cyclospondylous sharks) by some authorities, and are an ancient group. Their ancestors are well known from rocks of the Devonian Period, about 350 million years ago. These ancient fishes were remarkably like their modern descendants in form, in the possession of open gill slits, numerous teeth, and wide, fleshy pectoral fins. Their dominance of the seas may have been challenged by huge reptiles such as ichthyosaurs and mosasaurs, but they outlived these monsters. Today some of them have the reputation of being the most feared and savage predators in the seas, excepting only the very sharklike killer whale, a mammal that exceeds most sharks in size and all of them in ferocity (*See under Whale*).

Twelve families of sharks include all of the species commonly found along the coasts of the United States and Canada. All have five pairs of gill slits, except the offshore frilled shark, which has one family to itself, and the sixgill and sevengill sharks, together in another family. The frilled shark is an offshore, deepwater species, identified by the six gill slits, with the first of these continued completely under the neck. The sevengill occurs offshore on the Pacific Coast, and in San Francisco Bay. The sixgill occurs on both Atlantic and Pacific coasts. It is usually found in deep water, and may exceed 17 feet in length.

The largest shark is the whale shark, a slow-moving, 45-foot giant that feeds on small fishes, squids, and crustaceans. It is spotted, blunt-headed, and generally found in warm seas.

The hammerheads are bizarre—the head is flattened and drawn out to both sides; nostrils and eyes are at the extremities. The tooth-studded mouth is well under the head. The great hammerhead, found only in the Atlantic, can be 15 feet long, and weigh 1,500 pounds. It is fast and dangerous, as are the smooth hammerhead and the scalloped hammerhead, both slightly smaller, and living in waters of both the Atlantic and

Pacific coasts. The bonnethead has a more rounded "hammer," seldom reaches 6 feet, and is not considered dangerous.

The nurse shark, common in shallow waters of the Atlantic, has two barbels, or feelers, near the nostrils. Largely tropical, it is seldom seen north of the Carolinas, and is not considered dangerous unless provoked. Large individuals may be eight feet long.

The horn shark, a Pacific species, seldom exceeds five feet in length. It has two heavy spines, one in front of each dorsal fin, and its dental plates curve upward (upper jaw) and downward (lower jaw), giving it a porcine expression and the nickname of pig shark.

The sand shark, an Atlantic Coast species, may be 10 feet long. It has a ferocious aspect, but is not known to be dangerous to humans. It has a thick body and a narrow, tapering head (*See under Fish*).

Dogfish, with six species in the Atlantic Ocean and two of them in the Pacific, have spines in front of each dorsal fin, as does the horn shark, but they are without the anal fin, which the horn shark has. The common dogfish has a poison gland for each dorsal spine. A large shark of this group may be four feet long.

There is one species of angel shark in waters of both the Atlantic and Pacific coasts. Seldom longer than five feet. the angel shark inhabits shallow water. Its body is flattened, as is the head, but it has the gill slits on the sides, and not underneath as the rays have them. They are not known to attack swimmers.

Cat sharks are generally under three feet long, and are often spotted or striped. They have two dorsal fins. When taken from the water, they inflate themselves with air; if thrown back, they often experience difficulty in expelling the air, and float helplessly for hours. Three species of Pacific waters,

include the swell shark and two of the Atlantic Ocean species, belong in this family.

The largest group of sharks are those in the requiem family (Galeidae). The name is believed to be derived from the observation that once one of the large sharks of this order attacked a victim, the only task remaining was to hold a requiem, a mass for the dead. While not all of the 28 species living in the warmer waters of the United States are dangerous, many are extremely so. The tiger, leopard, and blue sharks are very dangerous to swimmers. The tiger shark, in American waters, reaches 18 feet; specimens 30 feet long have been taken elsewhere. All have the upper tail fin prolonged about twice as far as the lower.

Soupfin sharks, among the relatively harmless species of requiems, were caught for their vitamin-rich liver; they seldom exceed 6½ feet. Blacktip, white-tip, lemon, and roundtip sharks are also small requiems.

The mackerel sharks, so called because of their high streamlining and great speed, contain the huge (to 45 feet) basking shark, an inoffensive feeder on plankton; the 20-foot threshers with the greatly exaggerated tail fin and apparent reluctance to injure humanity; and the fierce white, mako, porbeagle, and salmon sharks. The white shark is also known as the maneater; the record length for this species is 36½ feet, but most individuals are only 20 to 25 feet, and may weigh 3½ tons. Makos are smaller, up to twelve feet, averaging under ten feet in length. The porbeagle (Atlantic) and the salmon shark (Pacific) are about ten feet long, and, while not known to be dangerous to humans, are suspect of being so. Except for the threshers, mackerel sharks have tails with equal upper and lower fins.

### Rays and Skates

Rays and skates (*see also under Skate*) have greatly enlarged pectoral fins that

*Common skate*

are attached to the head and extend far down the body. The gills are on the underside of the fish; those that live above the bottom breathe through the mouth and out through the gills, as do other fishes, while the bottom dwellers draw water in through the spiracles, openings on the upper side near the eyes.

Seven families of rays live in the waters of the Atlantic and Pacific oceans along the coasts of North America. They are sawfishes, guitarfishes, skates, and electric rays, stingrays, eagle rays, and the manta rays. Sawfishes, found only in the Atlantic, use the tooth-studded rostrum to dig in sand and to wound schooling fish for later consumption. They are subtropical and tropical in distribution. The record length is about 35 feet. Guitarfishes, of both coasts, seem to be somewhere between sharks and rays in the degree of flatness. They are seldom longer than six feet.

There are 22 species of skates in the waters off the coasts of United States and Canada. Superficially, the chief difference between them and the rays is in the length of the snout, which is longer in the skates. Skates are bottom feeders, eating crustaceans and echinoderms, and they are not harmful to humans. Some species are considered to be edible.

An electric ray can discharge 200 volts from the modified muscle tissue in its "wings." The electricity is used as its defense and to stun the small fishes on which it feeds. The bodies of the electric rays are round as seen from above, without the snout that distinguishes the skates.

Stingrays, of 11 species, 7 in the Atlantic and 4 in the Pacific, have very long tails with teeth all along the backbone. One of these is enlarged, and is equipped with a venom gland. It can be driven into the flesh of a victim with great force by the swinging tail. In American waters stingrays are usually less than four feet across the wings, more commonly about two.

Eagle rays, identifiable by the roll of flesh at the front of the head, which appears as a thick upper lip, also have the sharp spine and the venom gland as in the stingrays. They have large, flat teeth, and can crush large clams with apparent ease. The tail is very long and thin, and the poison spine is near the body. There are four species in the Atlantic, and one, the bat stingray, in the Pacific. The largest is about seven feet wide.

*Bat stingray*

Manta rays pursue and catch fishes near the surface, and have feeding fins on either side of the mouth. They range in size from about 2 feet across to 22 feet. Mantas often jump out of the water, landing with a tremendous splash, possibly to stun their prey. There are two species in the Atlantic, three in the Pacific.

The chimera, or ratfish, is common in the Pacific. About three feet long, with a thin, ratlike tail, it has a spine and a painful venom. It prefers deep water, and sometimes occurs in large numbers.                        —G.B.S.

*Recommended Reading*

**Field Book of Marine Fishes of the Atlantic Coast**—C.M. Breder, Jr. G.P. Putnam's Sons, New York.
**Living Fishes of the World**—Earl S. Herald. Doubleday & Company, Garden City, New York.

*Birds of the open sea, sooty shearwaters visit lonely islands to lay a single egg*

## SHEARWATER
### Sooty Shearwater
**Other Common Names** — Black hag, dark-bodied shearwater
**Scientific Name** — *Puffinus griseus*
**Family** — Procellariidae (shearwaters and fulmars)
**Order** — Procellariiformes
**Size** — Length, 16 to 18 inches
**Range** — Breeds in southern hemisphere; a summer migrant offshore on both Atlantic and Pacific coasts

The commonest shearwater off the North American coast, the sooty shearwater is about the size of a laughing gull but appears to be completely dark. The wings are longer and narrower than those of a gull of that size, and the characteristic flight is a stiff-winged glide only inches above the surface of the water.

The only link that the shearwaters have retained with the land is their nesting requirement of burrows on lonely islands free of four-footed predators. After an incubation period of nearly two months, the single chick is fed for another 3½ months; then, abandoned by the parents, it finds its own way to the water and a life at sea.

Sooty, Audubon's, greater, and Cory's shearwaters have been seen along the Atlantic Coast; sooty, slender-billed, pale-footed, Manx, pink-footed, and New Zealand shearwaters on the Pacific Coast.

The fulmar is more gull-like than the other shearwaters. Inhabiting the colder water along both coasts, it also lives on fishes and marine wastes. It glides and banks in typical shearwater fashion. The plumage is light gray all over in the dark phase, but in the light phase it has gray wings with a white head, body, and tail. The fulmar's tail is short, and its feet project out beyond it when the bird flies.

Shearwaters, fulmars, albatrosses, and petrels have nostrils that are encased in short tubes. Another trait they possess in common is the manufacture of stomach oils from the food they eat and on which they feed the young. Some species, as a defense, eject this oil, nutritious but foul-smelling, with accuracy up to five feet. —G.B.S.

*Bighorn sheep rams inhabit high, inaccessible, mountainous terrain*

## SHEEP
### North American Bighorns or Mountain Sheep

There are two species of mountain sheep native to North America, the Rocky Mountain sheep *Ovis canadensis*, or bighorn, as it is more familiarly known, and the Dall's sheep, *Ovis dalli*. In Kamchatka and northern Siberia the Asiatic bighorn, *Ovis nivicola*, occurs. This is a very close relative of the American sheep.

The Rocky Mountain bighorn is undoubtedly the most coveted prize of American sportsman. When much hunted, it becomes one of the most keenly alert of all the American big game. As it lives among the loftiest peaks, the task of stalking this animal is one of the most arduous and also one of the most scenic types of hunting that exists. The royal head, with its heavy curling horns—which have been recorded up to 49½ inches in measurement around the outside curve and 16 7/8 inches in circumference at the base—makes a most desirable hunter's trophy.

The Rocky Mountain bighorn is both a browser and a grazer. Throughout the warmer seasons of the year the older rams, and the ewes accompanied by the younger rams, are in separate parties—the older rams inhabiting the higher, more inaccessible terrain, the ewes and younger rams, the lower slopes. The lambs are born in late May or June and generally number one or two. After a few days in hiding they are strong enough to follow their mother over the steep mountain trails.

In late fall both the rams and ewes move to the lower levels and the valleys where they can find protection from the winter's storms. During December some of the old rams seek the company of the ewes but by January they are generally back with their former companions.

The true Rocky Mountian bighorn, *Ovis canadensis canadensis*, is found in southwestern Alberta and northeastern British Columbia south of the

Peace River, and south through the Rocky Mountains to northern New Mexico. To the east in the Badlands of North and South Dakota, western Nebraska, eastern Montana, and Wyoming, the Badlands bighorn. *Ovis canadensis auduboni*, occurred. This subspecies of the Rocky Mountain bighorn was supposed to carry longer and narrower horns and is now believed to be extinct.

South and west of the Rocky Mountain bighorn's range, there are a number of subspecies with somewhat different habits, and these are recognizable by their larger ears. They live on the dry, semidesert mountains of the southwestern United States, and northern Mexico, and are known as desert sheep. In many places which they inhabit, water is not found throughout much of the year, and they quench their thirst with the water-storing cacti, such as the barrel cactus and the giant saguaro (*See under Cactus*). The sheep are said to butt these cacti down to get at the moisture they contain.

The Rimrock bighorn, *Ovis canadensis californiana*, which was formerly found from southern British Columbia south to central California, has recently been classified by mammalogists as in the desert sheep group, chiefly on account of its long ears. It is now very local and has been greatly reduced in numbers. Other desert sheep are Nelson's bighorn, *Ovis canadensis nelsoni*, of the desert ranges of southeastern California and southern Nevada; the Mexican bighorn, *Ovis canadensis mexicana*, of Arizona, western New Mexico, western Texas, and northern Mexico; the lower California bighorn, *Ovis canadensis weemsi*, of southern Baja California.

The Dall's sheep, or white sheep, *Ovis dalli*, inhabits the mountains of Alaska, the Yukon, and northern British Columbia. Two subspecies are recognized. The true white sheep is easily recognized by its white coat. It is slightly smaller in size than the Rocky Mountain sheep and has more slender horns. Its habits are much the same as those of the bighorn.

On the Kenai Peninsula in Alaska there is a small white sheep, the Kenai sheep, *Ovis dalli kenaiensis*, which had been named as a subspecies of the main Alaskan form.

In the southern Yukon and northern British Columbia a dark, blackish-brown subspecies of Dall's sheep occurs, which is known as Stone's sheep, *Ovis dalli stonei*. The white sheep of northern Yukon gradually intergrade into the dark sheep of the south. Some of the flocks of central Yukon may contain animals of varying amounts of dark and light color. One from near Dawson City was described as a new species, *Ovis fannini*. It was described as being white and covered with a gray blanket. However, being actually only a gradation, Fannin's sheep is considered synonymous with Dall's sheep.

—T.D.C.

## SHENANDOAH NATIONAL PARK
**Location**—Northern Virginia
**Size**—302 square miles
**Mammals**—Deer, bobcats, foxes, raccoons, squirrels, chipmunks, woodchucks, weasels, skunks, rabbits
**Birdlife**—Ravens, crows, hawks, owls, hummingbirds, many songbirds
**Plants**—Oaks, gums, locusts, sycamores, birches, ashes, elms, walnuts, maples, tulip trees, white and pitch pines, spruces, firs, yews, azaleas, mountain laurels, many wild flowers

The old, rounded, tree-covered mountains of the northern portion of Virginia's Blue Ridge are a part of the Appalachian Range—the backbone of the eastern half of the continent. The highest peak, Hawksbill Mountain, is 4,049 feet above sea level, and looks down on the fertile Shenandoah Valley far below.

The park is narrow, from 2 to 13 miles wide, but 75 miles long. More than 400 families lived on the land

*Shenandoah National Park, Virginia, is located in the Blue Ridge Mountains*

when it became a park in 1935. The region had been lumbered, but most of it has regained its former wilderness aspect.

The Blue Ridge Parkway joins Shenandoah and Great Smoky Mountain National Park.

**Accommodations**—Lodges, cabins, and campgrounds

**Headquarters**—At Luray, Virginia

### SHINER

Many fishes are commonly called shiners. The true shiners, however, are the fishes of the genus *Notropis*. There are a great number of different species of shiners within this genus and to add to the confusion, many of them resemble each other so closely that they are extremely difficult to distinguish from one another. Besides the common shiner *Notropis cornutus*; a few other shiners include the pugnose, *Notropis anogenus*; the emerald, *Notropis atherinoides*; and the broadstripe, *Notropis euryzonus*.

**Common Shiner**

**Other Common Names**—Northern common shiner, central common shiner

**Scientific Name**—*Notropis cornutus*

**Family**—Cyprinidae (minnows and carps)

**Order**—Cypriniformes

**Size**—Length, rarely over eight inches
**Range**—Freshwater streams throughout numerous scattered areas of the United States.

The common shiner has one dorsal fin which has from 8 to 10 complete rays and one incomplete ray in front. The fish's tail fin is forked. Its mouth is toothless but teeth are present in the throat. Its snout is rounded and its eyes are very large.

The common shiner is steely blue, sometimes with dark horizontal lines on its back. Its most useful function is as food for larger species of fishes. The common shiner, like most shiners, is used extensively by fishermen as bait.
—M.R.

## SHOOTING STAR
**Henderson's Shooting Star**
**Other Common Names**—Mosquito bills
**Scientific Name**—*Dodecatheon hendersonii*
**Family**—Primulaceae (primrose family)
**Range**—British Columbia to central California on the Pacific slope east to eastern Washington, Idaho, and eastern Oregon
**Habitat**—Slopes, especially in open woods, Upper Sonoran and Transition Zones
**Time of Blooming**—March to May

Henderson's shooting star, quite general over California, wakes with the first warm days in low altitudes, following spring up into the mountains, where it blooms in July and August in Sierra meadows at 10,000 feet elevation, in the San Bernardino and San Jacinto mountains of the south and in the north Coast Ranges from Humboldt to Siskiyou. Great companies of the alpine shooting stars, *Dodecatheon alpinum*, stand here, frequently with their feet in the snow water that melts during the short day from the towering peaks around. The color is commonly lavender or purple, the base bearing markings of white, yellow, and purple in

*Henderson's shooting star*

bands, but an almost white one is found along coastal southern California—*Dodecatheon clevelandii*. A yellow species, more rare, comes from the hills of Mariposa, probably drawing its color from the gold-filled dust of earlier days.

The long petals turning immediately back give to this flower the common names of sailor's cap, wild cyclamen, mosquito bills.

## SHOREBIRD
The term *shorebird* refers to the small wading birds: the sandpipers, plovers, stilts, phalaropes, oystercatchers, and others that inhabit the shore. All of them belong to the order Charadriiformes, as do the gulls and auks, which are not generally included in the shorebird category. (*See Sandpiper; Plover; Phalarope; and Oystercatcher*) —G.B.S.

## SHREW

The smallest of all living mammals are the shrews. In general they are diminutive little creatures with long mobile snouts, minute eyes, short limbs, and soft fur. While their eyesight is poor, their other senses are sharp and highly developed. In general, shrews are extremely pugnacious and will unhestitatingly attack and kill a creature twice their own size. They are primarily insectivorous and, in order to meet their energy needs and high rate of metabolism, must feed constantly day and night. From sunrise to sunset they favor shady nooks and subterranean passageways but under cover of darkness will forage abroad in the open.

American shrews can be divided into two principal groups, the long-tailed shrews and the short-tailed shrews. There are about thirty-nine species of long-tailed shrews that vary in certain characteristics and habits, but are generally the same.

The masked, or cinerous, shrew, *Sorex cinerous*, is perhaps the commonest and the one usually seen. This tiny, slender long-tailed species is found over most of the northern half of North America and is so high-strung that it usually dies from shock a few minutes after its capture.

Of all our shrews the water shrew, *Sorex palustris*, is the most outstanding. It is at home in the mountain streams and lakes and can swim and dive with an even greater skill than our better known aquatic mammals. The water shrew has the distinction of being the only mammal that can actually walk and run on the surface film of the water. For the best demonstration of this remarkable feat, the shrew needs the surface of the water glassy smooth. The hairs on its feet hold little globules of air that act as pontoons. Swimming under water, its coat is encased in a silvery layer of air that glistens like a silvery fish as it darts about submerged rocks in search of freshwater crustaceans

and aquatic insects. The water shrew is relatively a giant among the American long-tailed shrews and is about the size of a house mouse. Its hind feet are enlarged and fringed with hair for swimming and its long tail is compressed vertically.

The pigmy shrew, *Microsorex hoyi*, is not only the smallest shrew, but the smallest of all the mammals in America. Adult specimens may weigh no more than two grams. Although separated generically in its classification from the more common and better known shrews, it bears a close resemblance to them.

In addition to having a shorter tail, the short-tailed shrew, *Blarina brevicauda*, is more robust and hardier than the long-tailed species. Relative to its size it is the most ferocious and bloodthirsty of all our mammals, devouring large quantities of insects daily, and even killing animals twice its own size. Moist brushland is the choice habitat

of this shrew. It loves to tunnel under decaying leaves and in soft loose soil in search of insect life. The bite of the short-tailed shrew has a mild toxic effect sufficient to stupefy a large mouse but not enough to inconvenience a human being. The range of the short-tailed shrew covers most of the eastern half of the United States and southern Canada. (*See also under Mammal*)

—G.G.G.

**Masked Shrew**
**Other Common Names** — Common shrew, cinerous shrew
**Scientific Name** — *Sorex cinereus*
**Family** — Soricidae (shrews)
**Order** — Insectivora
**Size** — Body length, 3 to 4¼ inches; tail, 1¼ to 1¾ inches; weight, about ¼ ounce
**Range** — Alaska and Canada from Arctic Ocean and Hudson Bay (except extreme northern Quebec) south to Washington, Idaho, central Utah (to any border), central Colorado, and north-central New Mexico, central Nebraska, Iowa, eastern Illinois, Kentucky, and Virginia. Southern extension along borders of Tennessee and North Carolina to Georgia

More action is condensed into the tiny shrew's sixteen-month life than many larger creatures ever experience. Under the grass and ground litter that canopy its little trails, it darts and scurries in a year-round search for food. Although a shrew's eyesight is poor, its sense of smell is good and it investigates every cranny with its flexible, twitching snout. It can eat its weight in insects every few hours, and often prey bigger than itself. Mice, snails, worms, dead animals, and occasional nuts and berries feed its insatiable appetite. The female shrew has particular reason for expending constant energy, for in a year she may raise 3 litters of 4 to 10 young each. Small wonder she sleeps but

*The short-tailed shrew is able to kill animals twice its own size*

momentarily. Her nest, a ball of grass or dry leaves, may be hidden under a log or in an abandoned burrow. Carnivores, from wolves to weasels, eat shrews, despite the little animal's strong odor. However, enough are left to populate all areas providing suitable food and shelter—from the new Jersey marshes to the Alaskan tundra. The shrew's importance as a destroyer of insects is important to man economically.

## Short-tailed Shrew
**Other Common Names**—Big short-tailed shrew, mole shrew
**Scientific Name**—*Blarina brevicauda*
**Family**—Soricidae (shrews)
**Other**—Insectivora
**Size**—Body length, 3¾ to 5 inches or more; tail, ¾ to 1 inch; weight, ½ to 1 ounce
**Range**—Eastern United States north to southern Canada and west to southeastern Saskatchewan, central North and South Dakota, Nebraska, northwestern Kansas, extreme northeastern Colorado, central Oklahoma, and eastern corner of Texas

### Habits of the Short-tailed Shrew
It is safe to say that most people have never seen a shrew. If they have it is usually only a brief glimpse of a mouselike creature rustling through some dead leaves; yet these little animals are all about us—in the woods, in the fields even alongside our houses. We do not see them because of their secretive habits and manner of working under cover, but most scientists agree that one species, the short-tailed shrew, is the commonest mammal in eastern North America.

The Ojibway and Cree Indians labeled this shrew *kin-skee-sha-wah-bee-gah-note-see*, meaning sharp-nosed, short-tailed field mouse. Actually the shrew is not a mouse at all but an insectivore related to the common mole. Its tiny eyes, lack of external ears, and strong front feet adapt the shrew to a burrowing mode of life, and most of it is spent tunneling through the forest or meadow floor in search of earthworms, insects, and small vertebrates. They also eat plant food, and captive shrews will even eat crackers and walnuts. Because of its high rate of metabolism (food-burning) the shrew is a slave to its appetite and must eat a large amount of food to keep alive. However, accounts of its eating two or three times its weight in a day are probably exaggerated. Captive short-tailed shrews seldom eat more than seven grams of food a day—less than half their weight.

Sleep for the shrew is a matter of an hour here and an hour there and the little animals do not stay still for long, even while asleep. They wake up every few minutes to change position and to clean themselves before dozing off for another brief nap. They may sleep on their stomachs, on their sides, or even on their backs with all four legs in the air. They usually sleep in one of their elaborate underground tunnels but may occasionally catch a nap above ground.

The short-tailed shrew is an accomplished digger and constructs underground tunnels that serve as shelter and hunting grounds. With rapid motions of the powerful front feet working alternately, the shrew makes a short vertical tunnel. The loosened dirt is kicked to the surface with the hind feet. After digging down several inches the little miner begins a horizontal tunnel. When a load of dirt has accumulated behind it, the shrew turns a somersault and pushes the dirt to the end of the horizontal tunnel with its nose. It continues on up to the surface losing most of the dirt on the way. Undaunted, the shrew again enters the vertical tunnel and kicks the already loosened dirt to the surface with its hind feet. In this manner the shrew is able to dig in hard-packed soil at the rate of an inch a minute. Pebbles and other obstructions are firmly grasped in its teeth and tugged to the surface. From time to time, the shrew smooths out the mound of soil at the tunnel entrance with its nose and front feet.

The short-tailed shrew is commonly thought to vary its insectivorous diet with mice and other small mammals. Actually it is unable to catch mice unless these happen to enter its underground tunnels. On the surface, mice are able to elude a shrew with ease. In a very small cage, where shrews are kept for observations and experiments, it may be a different story, especially if the shrew is an aggressive individual. The shrew first grabs the mouse in the midsection and the combatants roll about the cage floor in a brief scuffle. The mouse may break loose for a moment but the shrew immediately grabs it by the hindquarters and allows itself to dragged about the cage as the mouse desperately struggles to break free. The shrew then releases its hold but instantly grabs the mouse by the back and delivers several telling bites on head and body.

It is important to remember that a shrew-mouse battle occurs only in very small cages where the mouse has no room in which to maneuver. In large cages the mouse is always too agile for the shrew and can elude it easily. Shrews show a great deal of individuality in their reactions towards mice and some will not attack a mouse, even in a very small cage. Oliver Pearson, an expert on shrew behavior, gives the following interesting information on this point:

"I can remember when I was taking movies of shrews killing meadow mice. I wasted yards of film on one *Blarina* that was terrified everytime the mouse came near it; another one made only half-hearted attacks, and a third attacked so fast and so viciously that I missed most of the action."

Are shrews sociable animals? The bulk of the scientific literature certainly suggests that they are not. Should two pugnacious individuals meet in the course of their daily activities, they face each other with open mouths and give several shrill, penetrating squeaks. One may throw back its head and send forth a loud, birdlike chatter of rage. If one does not retreat, the shrews fly at each other and go into a clinch, rolling about the ground and biting each other on head and body. When they break apart they are frequently minus several chunks of fur, and one may be killed if the fighting continues.

On the other hand there is some evidence that shrews are somewhat socially inclined. Mammalogists have often trapped several in the same tunnel, and five shrews, of both sexes, have lived happily together in capitivity. They slept, curled together, and frequently nuzzled one another. The sociability of the short-tailed shrew seems to depend primarily upon individual dispositions. Some live peacefully together; others fight on sight. Perhaps age and sex play important roles in the social life of this animal, but this has not yet been determined.

Like many of even our commonest mammals, we really know very little about the life history of the shrew. How well can it see? How many litters of young does it have each year? Why does it die so quickly in live-traps? The answers to these and many other questions are still unknown. There is still much to be learned about this little dweller of the underground.  —J.P.R.

## SHRIKE
**Loggerhead Shrike**
**Other Common Names**—Butcher-bird, French mockingbird
**Scientific Name**—*Lanius ludovicianus*
**Family**—Laniidae (shrikes)
**Order**—Passeriformes
**Size**—Length, nine inches
**Range**—Southern Canada, south-central Maine, and southwestern New Brunswick south to Baja California, the Gulf

*The loggerhead shrike is easily identified by its black facial mask*

Coast and southern Florida to central Mexico

The loggerhead shrike is a bird of very pronounced character and, wherever it lives it occupies a conspicuous place among the feathered folk of the countryside. Although members of the great order to which songbirds belong, shrikes, have certain hawklike habits that set them apart from other passerine birds. The loggerhead shrike is a keen hunter and makes quick, fierce sallies after its prey from a perch on some dead treetop or telegraph pole, or post or hedge by the roadside. Many grasshoppers, crickets, and other large insects are caught and devoured. Now and then larger quarry is obtained, such as lizards, small birds, and mice.

The voice of the loggerhead shrike is harsh and metallic. During the mating season it indulges in numerous attempts to sing, but all its efforts fall short of being musical. The loggerhead shrike's ordinary call, however, is one of the familiar bird notes of the South and, in spite of its rasping quality, has a certain brave vigor about it that is pleasant to hear.

The nest is in low, thick trees or thorny hedges, and is constructed of strips of bark, twigs, and vegetable fibers, and lined with finer materials. From three to five creamy white eggs, spotted with brown and lavender, are laid.

**Northern Shrike**
**Other Common Names**—Butcher-bird, nine-killer, winter shrike
**Scientific Name**—*Lanius excubitor*
**Family**—Laniidae (shrikes)
**Order**—Passeriformes
**Size**—Length, 10¼ inches
**Range**—From northern limit of tree growth south to the northern region of British Columbia, Alberta, and central Saskatchewan. In winter south to northern California, central Nevada, central Arizona, New Mexico, southern Kansas, central Illinois, Indiana, Ohio, Pennsylvnia, northern Virginia, and Maryland. In Old World from northern limit of tree growth south to North Africa, India, North China, and Japan

Our native shrikes are much alike in appearance and food habits. Both the northern, and the loggerhead shrike

*Northern shrike*

## SHRUB

A woody plant with more than one stem and less than 12 feet tall is usually classified by botanists as a shrub. A tree, by comparison, has, at maturity, normally only one trunk, a more or less definitely formed crown of leaves, and a height of more than 12 feet.

The lack of uniformity of growth in the different species of trees often contravenes classifications of them as trees or shrubs based on numerical height. A tree that may top one hundred feet in rich bottomland may be a stunted, scraggly "shrub" on a dry hillside. There are also exceptions to the rule that a tree cannot have more than one trunk, as a large willow often has several trunks of tree size. The gray birch, *Betula populifolia* (*see under Birch*), often has many stems, or trunks, sprouting from the base.  —G.B.S.

### Fruits of Some Native Shrubs

Throughout the fall and winter North American woodlands and gardens gradually become bare. On many shrubs and trees the fruits cling to the twigs late into the winter. Anyone who has seen the bright orange of a heavily fruiting winterberry, *Ilex verticillata*, contrasted against a snowy background, knows how much the berried plants add to the beauty of the winter woods.

The fruits of various plants provide one of the greatest sources of food for many kinds of fruit-eating birds. When the ground is hard and frozen so that birds cannot find insects and seeds of low plants, the birds will flock to areas where plants with berries are abundant. It is interesting that so many native fruiting shrubs have been and are being used by housewives of today and yesterday in making jams and jellies.

### Red berried Shrubs

Winterberry, *Ilex verticillata*. In the fall and early winter, after the leaves are gone, the winterberry shrub attracts

that ranges farther south, are often called butcher-bird. It is interesting to note that the shrikes, alone of all the great group of passerine birds, have solved the problem of utilizing as food, animals too large to be swallowed whole. Like all of our songbirds of the passerine group, the shrikes have small feet adapted to walking, hopping and perching, but too weak to be used as weapons. Therefore, shrikes must kill their prey with their bills. This unique habit enables them to solve the difficult problem of tearing their prey into pieces small enough to be swallowed. Since shrikes are unable to hold their prey with their feet, as birds of prey do, they have developed the trick of wedging the victim in the fork of a branch or impaling it on some sharp object—a thorn, nail, or barb of a barbed wire fence.

Shrikes are wholly carnivorous. Their food consists of large insects, small mammals, birds, reptiles, and even fishes

notice. Then the brilliant scarlet berries gleam on slender, light gray twigs. Winterberry grows in wet soil and is a dioecious plant with male and female flowers growing on separate plants. Hence both male and female plants are necessary to obtain the berries which remain nearly the entire winter and are so useful as food for the birds. Winterberry has been carelessly harvested for Christmas decoration and should be protected.

Flowering raspberry, *Rubus odoratus*. An alternate-branching, eight-foot shrub, the stems covered with short brown hairs. Bark on the one-year twigs is loose and shaggy, peeling off easily in strips. The fruit grows in clusters on bristly stems.

Spicebush *Lindera benzoin*. A tall, shapely plant, abundant in moist woods, spicebush is one of our most common shrubs. The tender, green twigs arranged alternately on the stems are very aromatic when bruised, and the shining, oval, red berries appearing in September in small groups of three to five are spicy and aromatic, distinguishing the shrub at all times of the year. Spicebush was formerly used medicinally and is still used in certain cosmetics.

Staghorn sumac, *Rhus typhina*. One of our most brilliantly leafed autumn shrubs, it may be distinguished in winter by its alternate leaf scars nearly surrounding the silky buds. The stems are densely covered with hair. The small, dry drupes are borne in a terminal compound cluster and are dark red, covered with hairs. These fruits are pleasantly acid to the taste and a lemonadelike drink can be made by steeping the fresh fruit in water and then straining. Many birds eat the seeds of sumacs.

American yew, *Taxus canadensis*. This native evergreen shrub may be identified by the uniform green of the

*The fruits of staghorn sumac are an important winter food for a variety of song-birds, gamebirds, and small mammals*

*The blossoms of blueberry are delicate white bells*

twigs and undersides of the needles that are arranged spirally around the branches. The fruit, not a true berry, is a bright red, fleshy cup containing one black seed. It is most attractive against the deep green foliage. American yew is dioecious. It does well in shady areas. The wood is very tough and was used by the Indians in making bows.

*Blue-berried Shrubs*

Lowbush blueberry, *Vaccinium pennsylvanicum.* A low, rambling shrub with prominent, light green twigs, found growing in fields in sandy soil or along dry ledges in the woods. The ripe berries are a deep blue covered with a whitish bloom. Next to the sumacs, this shrub gives us the most vivid leaf coloring in the woods in autumn. The leaves turn color early whereupon whole fields are gloriously transformed into crimson, bronze, and scarlet.

Highbush blueberry, *Vaccinium corymbosum.* This is a much taller shrub than the lowbush blueberry and is from 4 to 10 feet in height. The ripe berries are larger, too, a purplish black, and are delicious to eat. They grow in clusters at the end of a short leafless branch of the previous year's growth.

Huckleberry, *Gaylussacia baccata.* This huckleberry is common in dry, sandy woods, growing two or three feet high. It may be distinguished from the blueberries by the numerous yellow, resinous dots on the under sides of the leaves. The ripe berry is purplish-black, is more seedy than the blueberries and less pleasing to the taste, but all three are used for making pies, jams, and jellies.

Maple-leaved viburnum, *Viburnum acerifolium.* An opposite branching shrub, four to five feet high, common in open woods or wood borders, with one-year twigs hairy at the tip. The fall coloring of the leaves is distincitive, being pale pink to purplish. Bluish-black berries, lasting late into the winter, are borne in terminal flat clusters on reddish, downy stems.

Nannyberry, *Viburnum lentago*. A considerably larger shrub than maple-leaved viburnum, with opposite branching stems, sometimes reaching the proportions of a small tree. The dark cadet-blue berries, sweet and edible, ripen in September and October on ruddy stems.

Hobblebush, *Viburnum alnifolium*. The name hobblebush is suggested by the appearance of the plant with its looping branches. A rather low, straggling shrub of cold mountain woods, it has large, heart-shaped leaves, sharply toothed and covered beneath with a rusty wool. The leaves turn maroon in the fall. The ovate fruits, borne in clusters on the hairy stems, are coral red, ripening to purple. Many other species of viburnums are attractive to birds because of the abundance of long-lasting fruit in fall, and the dense protective foliage in summer.

### White-berried Shrubs

Red osier dogwood, *Cornus stolonifera*. A straggling shrub, two to nine feet high, growing in wet places, often with willows and alders. Its bright red, shining stems are very attractive in winter. The white fruit is borne sparsely in small, flat clusters on the opposite branching stems.

Gray, or panicled, dogwood, *Cornus paniculata*. A low shrub which may be distinguished by the divergent, irregular branches and the light, orange-brown one-year twigs in sharp contrast to the gray, two-year twigs. The berries are white, borne in small bunches on pink stems. Many other dogwoods supply birds with food (See under Dogwood).

Bayberry, *Myrica carolinensis*. This shrub grows well both on uplands and at the seashore, and in acid soil. Its resinous dotted, aromatic leaves, persisting late into the fall, are thermostatic and curl, like the rhododendron, in cold weather. The hard, round, berrylike fruits are gray-white and waxy, appearing in thick clusters on the older part of the stems. In making the fragrant bayberry candles, the berries are steeped in boiling water and the wax skimmed off after cooling. Myrtle warblers and tree swallows are especially fond of the waxy berries of both the bayberry and its southern relative, the wax myrtle.

### Black-berried Shrubs

Wild blackberry, *Rubus allegheniensis*. An alternate-branching shrub, eight feet high, with reddish-brown stems bearing the old leaf bases through the winter. Thorns appear on the more vigorous shoots. The fruit is edible and is used in making pies, jams, and jellies. Blackberries are also eaten by many birds.

American elderberry, *Sambucus canadensis*. A tall shrub, reaching as high as 10 to 12 feet, with opposite, smooth, green branches having a white pith. This species has purplish-black berries in broad clusters and is widely used for making jams and jellies. The red-berried elder, *Sambucus pubens*, has red fruit in pyramidal-shaped clusters borne on stems with brown pith. The fruits are sought after and relished by many species of birds (*See also under Hedge; under Hedgerow; and under Plants and Water for Birds*).

*Recommended Reading*

**The Complete Garden**—Taylor and Cooper. Garden City Publishing Company, New York. **How to Know the Wild Fruits**—Maude G. Peterson. The Macmillan Company, New York. **Songbirds in Your Garden**—John K. Terres. Thomas Y. Crowell Company, New York.

### Some Native Spring-flowering Shrubs

After the comparative bleakness of the winter landscape, a fresh and delicate beauty comes back to the woods. As early as February the roots of trees and shrubs start to absorb great quantities of water, which is carried up through the trunk and branches to the fully formed but still tiny leaves and flowers. Many

*Gray dogwood has small white berries borne on pink stems*

shrubs unfold their leaves before the flowers open but several of the most beautiful show no green until the flowers have started to fade (*See Dogwood*).

Many beautiful native shrubs are cultivated around private homes, in school gardens, in botanical gardens, and in parks, where they are enjoyed by great numbers of people. Some are admired for the sake of their spring bloom; others because in autumn they have brilliant foliage or colorful fruits.

In open swamps, around lakes, and along streams, the native alders grow. About nine species of alders grow in the United States. One, the red alder, *Alnus rubra* of the Pacific Northwest, is a tree, usually 35 to 40 feet tall. In March, when the ice melts around their roots and warmer sunshine stimulates rising sap, the reddish-brown staminate flower catkins of the speckled alder lengthen into beautiful swinging yellow tassels. Winds blow the pollen from these to the crimson upright pistillate catkins and after the pollen grains grow down into the flower the little conelike fruits are formed. These cones persist through the next year. The alternate-growing, oval, dark green leaves appear after the early-spring blooming period. Alders are related to the birches and produce small seeds, eaten by goldfinches, pine siskins, and redpolls.

The American hazelnut, *Corylus americana*, which blooms at the same time as the speckled alder, *Alnus rugosa*, grows in open places or on sunny hillsides in sandy soil. Its staminate flower catkins are more slender than those of the alder and as they elongate they shed great quantities of yellow pollen which is carried by means of the wind to the pistillate flowers. From these pistillate flowers two chestnut-brown nuts develop, enclosed within a leaflike covering of bracts. These nuts are used as food both by man and by squirrels, mice, and other wild rodents. Grouse eat the catkins; rabbits, deer, and moose browse on the plants. There are two other species of hazelnuts growing in the

United States—the beaked hazelnut, *Corylus cornuta*, of the eastern United States, west to Kansas and Colorado; and another species of the Pacific coast region.

A common yellow-flowering shrub, with small fragrant flowers appearing before the leaves, is the spicebush, *Lindera benzoin*. It blooms in March or April about 10 days later than the speckled alder and American hazelnut. The spicebush grows abundantly in wet woods from Maine to North Carolina, west to Missouri and Kansas. The bark and leaves have a pleasant spicy odor when crushed, helping to make identification easy in all seasons. The branches, with their clusters of tiny, round buds, are often unnoticed in the winter woods but can be brought indoors for forcing. They make a lovely design silhouetted against a light background and later produce a mass of fragrant yellow blossoms. When fall comes the leaves turn golden yellow. The small, shining red fruits are not usually abundant but are very attractive. They are especially relished by the wood thrush, veery, and red-eyed vireo, also by catbirds and robins. Another species, the southern, or downy, spicebush, *L. mellissaefolia*, grows in the southeastern United States.

Several of the viburnums add their beauty to our woods in spring. Their oppositely placed leaves and branches are an aid in identifying this group. Three of the most common are—the blackhaw, *Viburnum prunifolium;* the nannyberry, also called sheepberry, *Viburnum lentago;* and the maple-leaved viburnum, *V. acerifolium*. All three blossom in May or June, the blackhaw a little before the others. All have similar small, white flowers growing in flat clusters, and dark blue fruits that are eaten by many birds. The nannyberry often grows in more moist places than

*The wild-raisin, a viburnum, has green berries that turn scarlet and then dark purple as they ripen*

the others and is more apt to be a tree. The maple-leaved viburnum is easily recognized since the form of its leaf is very much like that of a maple tree. Its fall leaf coloring is very distinctive with a pinkish cast rather than the orange or red of so many trees and shrubs.

Another shrub or small tree that blooms in April and May is the shadbush, or serviceberry, *Amelanchier canadensis*, widespread in the eastern United States. The flowers appear before the leaves have fully unfolded and the delicate beauty of this graceful, slender shrub stands out prominently on rocky hillsides, in open woodlands, or bordering streams. Shadbush, with its clustered flowers with five narrow white petals, and later, purplish-black edible berries, is a member of the rose family. Four or five species of shadbushes, or serviceberries grow in the East, fifteen to twenty in the West. Squirrels, chipmunks, and even black bears eat the fruits, and deer browse on the foliage.

A great many of the shrubs, cultivated as well as native, belong to the rose family. One, a very close relative of the apple, is the chokeberry of which there are several species that can be identified by the row of red-brown glands beside the midrib on the back of the leaf. Like the apple, the leaf of the chokeberry narrows abruptly to a point. Its white, clustered flowers are followed by bright red fruits that are eaten by grouse, some songbirds, and by black bears.

Anyone who has rambled through a sweetfern thicket on a sunny hillside, with the spicy fragrance all around, will never forget this plant. It is a small shrub, *Comptonia peregrina*, growing abundantly on dry slopes and borders of woods. It has narrow, dark green, fernlike leaves with rolled back edges. These characteristics may have given rise to the common name, sweetfern. Its inconspicuous flowers open early,

*Viburnum has small white blossoms that grow in flat clusters*

before the leaves. They are of two types, staminate and pistillate, often produced on separate plants. The pistillate flowers develop into the burlike fruits, each of which encloses a nutlet. Few animals are known to feed on the sweetfern, though deer browse on it; also gamebirds and rabbits make minor use of it. It grows from Canada and Minnesota south in the Appalachians to North Carolina and Georgia.

A plant family with many common representatives in northeastern United States is the heath, which contains among many other plants the blueberries, huckleberries, azaleas, laurels, and rhododendrons. Most of the native heaths grow in woods and swamps. The highbush blueberry is one of the most common of several species of blueberry. Its waxy, bell-like, sweet-scented white or pale pink flowers bloom in May. The light blue, edible fruits are enjoyed by birds and by many who have never seen the shrub growing, for they are sold in the markets. The brilliance of the foliage in autumn stands out vividly among the other fall colors. The tubular flowers of the pinxter-flower, or wild azalea, *Rhododendron nudiflorum,* open before the leaves in April or May. It is common in sandy or rocky woods from New York and New England south to Tennessee and South Carolina.

Among the evergreen members of the heath family are the mountain laurel, *Kalmia latifolia,* and the great laurel, or rhododendron, *Rhododendron maximum,* which grows from New England south to Georgia. In June it is worth a special trip to the woods to see the showy clusters of pinkish, waxy, bowl-shaped flowers of the mountain laurel. The numerous, gnarled and irregular branches are often linked with each other to form an almost impenetrable

*The red chokeberry is eaten by grouse, songbirds, and black bears*

thicket. The toothless, shiny, dark green leaves form a lovely color contrast to the pale flowers. The rhododendron is somewhat similar to the mountain laurel but a much larger plant with larger leaves and flowers, so that it creates a more handsome and showy mass. It generally grows in damper places and it is common to find ravines in mountainous regions near streams made practically impassable by rhododendron thickets. The shrub is native in the mountains of northwestern New Jersey and in large areas in similar regions from Lake Erie south to Georgia. The wild rhododendron flowers in late June or in July and a magnificent flowering of them may be seen in Great Smoky National Park of Tennessee and North Carolina.

*Recommended Reading*

**American Wildlife and Plants**—Alexander C. Martin et al. Dover Publications, New York. **The Book of Shrubs**—A.C. Hottes. Dodd, Mead & Company, New York.

**Field Book of American Trees and Shrubs**— F.S. Mathews. G.P. Putnam's Sons, New York. **Gray's Manual of Botany**—M.T. Fernald. American Book Company, New York. **Native Woody Plants of the United States**— W.R. Van Dersal, Misc., Pub. 303, United States Government Printing Office, Washington, D.C. **Our Northern Shrubs**—H. Keeler. Charles Scribner's Sons, New York. **Through Field and Woodland**—A.R. Northrop. G.P. Putnam's Sons, New York.

**SILK** (*See under Spider*)

**SIREN** (*See under Manatee; also under Amphibian*)

**SKATE**

The skate is a fish with huge pectoral fins attached from the back of the head to the beginning of the tail base, which is long and slender (about as long as the rest of the body) but with no discernible tail fin. There are two dorsal fins on the tail base instead of on the body. The body of a skate is so flattened that the pectorals extend outward and blend with

*The egg cases of skates are called devil's purses*

the body into a flat, disklike shape. There are a great many different species of skates. Although they strongly resemble stingrays, they do not have the large tail spine of the stingray and the stingray does not have dorsal fins on its tail (*See also under Sharks, Rays, and Chimera's; and under Fish*).

## Little Skate
**Other Common Names**—Common skate, hedgehog skate, tobacco box
**Scientific Name**—*Raja erinacea*
**Family**—Rajidae (skates)
**Order**—Rajiformes
**Size**—Length, 18 to 21 inches
**Range**—Waters off the Atlantic Coast of North America from northern Nova Scotia south to Virginia

The little skate is grayish to dark brown above. It usually has small dark spots at the edges of its pectoral fins. The lower portion of the fish is white or grayish.

Like all skates, the little skate lives at bay or ocean bottom. Its diet consists largely of crabs, bottom-dwelling shrimps, and squids. It bites readily at the hook and is probably the species of skate most caught by fishermen. Skates are of little value as either food or sport, however, and are usually returned to the sea.                      —M.R.

## SKIMMER
### Black Skimmer
**Other Common Names**—Scissorbill, shearwater
**Scientific Name**—*Rynchops nigra*
**Family**—Rynchopidae (skimmers)
**Order**—Charadriiformes
**Size**—Length, 16 to 19 inches
**Range**—Nests locally along the Atlantic and Gulf coasts from Massachusetts to Texas and Yucatan, Mexico; on the Pacific Coast from northwestern Mexico south to the Straits of Magellan

### Bird with the Strange Bill
Samuel de Champlain, early adventurer, came upon a bird in Nauset Harbor, Massachusetts, the form of whose bill was "a matter of astonishment." The upper mandible was "shorter by a third" than the lower one. Undoubtedly, Champlain wondered how it was possible for the creature to eat.

Unquestionably many people would wonder how such a bird could eat, if one should suddenly come into one's possession—a new form of life never seen or heard of before. Perhaps one would spend little time admiring the sleekness of its black upper plumage and the sharply contrasted whiteness of its underparts, the handsome ternine pinions, and the dainty feet of orange-vermilion. More likely he would spend most of his time examining the unique bill with this thought in mind. One would notice readily the unequal length of the two mandibles (actually differing by a fifth) and the fact that the upper one is sharply pointed; the lower one, laterally compressed and bluntly pointed.

The bill of this bird is, in reality, a distinctive feature, and with it is associated a peculiar habit. One might watch the bird flying low above the surf of an ocean's beach somewhere along the Atlantic Coast almost any summer day. Going along in the moving trough between two incoming breakers, it immerses the tip of its longer lower mandible in the water and deftly cuts the rippled surface. When once this trough has flattened out on the shore, the bird swings out to follow the next one approaching. Once again it cleaves the water with its bill with the sureness of one long apprenticed.

"I call it *skimmer,* from the manner of its collecting its food with the lower mandible as it flies along the surface of the water." Thus an English naturalist, Thomas Pennant, in bestowing a name on this bird in 1773, tersely explained this habit. He believed, in other words, that the lower mandible scooped up organic matter as it cut the surface. Naturalists in later years corroborated this view by numerous observations. But today the interpretation of these obser-

*Black skimmer from Audubon's* Elephant Folio

vations is being questioned. Exactly how does the modified bill aid in securing food, if it aids at all?

One might see a skimmer, flying along the water's surface with its mouth open and the tip of the lower mandible immersed, suddenly thrust its entire beak forward into the water and retrieve a glistening fish crosswise between its mandibles. Stanley C. Arthur of Louisiana has noted that skimmers feed while standing in shallow water, fishing in the manner of herons, and he accounts for the water-cutting habit as being a nervous reaction, having no bearing on feeding. Robert Cushman Murphy, however, an expert on oceanic birds, came to the conclusion that the flattened lower mandible is a "lure." Thus small fishes might be attracted to the surface of the water either by the brilliant color of the skimmer's bill or by the circulation it produces, whence they are caught by the bird on retracing its course. It is obvious, in the face of these varied observations and views, that the question has not been definitely answered.

Three closely related species of skimmers are known to scientists—one in America, one in Africa, and one in Asia. All are immediately distinguishable by the knifelike bill.

Along the Atlantic Coast of North America dwells the black skimmer—the *Rynchops nigra nigra* of science. Tropic-loving, generally preferring the sultry Caribbean Sea to temperate climes, certain of its numbers, with the advent of the northern spring, venture to the areas on the southeastern coast of the United States to rear their young. One such place is Cardwell Island, a narrow, low-lying bit of land located eight miles off the coast of Cape Charles, Virginia.

Should you desire to see this skimmer at home in its isolated environs, visit this lonely sandy islet on a bright day late in June. A treat is in store for you.

Eight hundred black skimmers claim insignificant Cardwell Island as their residence during the summer months.

Yet the pungent saltmarsh that fringes its western shore remains unoccupied, while the seaside sparrows have for themselves the grass-tufted sand dunes that form the central ridge. In fact, it is only a small portion of the broad eastern sand beach that is skimmer territory. There pairs nest close together in a semblance of harmony, some as near to each other as four feet.

Remarkable it is that such birds prefer to live in close quarters and tolerate one another's company rather than scatter themselves about over available territory and exist in isolated pairs where privacy is possible. It is likely that the skimmers have swallowed all personal feelings in regard to the matter and endure the inconveniences of colonial life for the sake of mutual protection against enemies. Instead of nesting alone, experience in past ages has taught the species that a hundred or more eyes are better for detecting danger than four, that a mass attack upon an enemy is more effective than an attack of two individuals. Hence the habit developed. Of course, the skimmer is not alone in having this manner of nesting. It is commonly seen in almost all seabirds.

Let us suppose you have actually decided to visit Cardwell Island. You are unused to the ways of the skimmer, even of colonial nesting birds. As you walk leisurely up the beach from the northern tip of the island, your attention is undoubtedly directed toward a number of these peculiar birds winging their way over the surf. On approaching the center of the island, eight hundred of the birds might suddenly rise into the air and begin circling madly in all directions. One will then hear for the first time their woebegone, houndlike yelps. He may also suddenly discover that the nearest skimmer may unexpectedly dash in his direction. Swiftly, accurately it aims for one's face. *Wush h h!* Luckily, at the last moment, just before striking, it swerves closely to one's right, giving an inappropriate, doleful *owk*. On comes an-

*Black skimmers nest in large numbers on isolated beaches*

other for the same target. But it carefully times a swoop upward, almost striking your forehead. The fusillade continues with the onslaught of one skimmer after another. Soon one realizes that all is a game of bluff. The attacks are futile, almost laughable. Assured, one strides boldly forward to determine the cause of the hubbub.

Now the skimmers are so terror-stricken that some are falling helplessly to the ground in seeming prostration. One lies on its belly with wings limply outstretched on the sand. Another rests on its side with one wing folded beneath and the other extended and waving weakly in the air. One's first impulse is to pick one of them up, for here is an opportunity to look over that odd bill. But no! As one moves toward the bird, it appears to summon all its strength and to drag itself away a few feet. If you follow, it soon flies away brusquely, leaving you to marvel at its speedy recovery. Most likely, in this commotion, you fail to see the unusual performance of several skimmers in the vicinity of one of the tidal pools. One in particular is splashing about desperately in the water. From all appearances it is "com-

ing up" for the last time. Why all this game of bluff anyway? There is a very good reason! Almost at your feet are six nests containing downy young. You have paid so much attention to the old birds that your attention has been diverted from them. Is this game of bluff an effective means of defense?

The nests of the black skimmer are mere depressions scraped by the birds in the yellowish sand and are without any vestige of lining. They are hollowed out in a comparatively simple manner. The old birds crouch on a chosen spot and turn around and around, at the same time throwing the pulverized soil backward with their webbed toes. Once the excavation is deep enough, the female of a mated pair soon lays an egg in it. Eager to undertake nesting responsibilities, the skimmer starts sitting upon it immediately. During each day thereafter another egg appears until four are ultimately laid. Three weeks later the hatching begins. Only one downy youngster pips its way out from a shell. The other young appear on successive days in the order in which the respective eggs were deposited. Pity the last chick to appear! It must struggle for survival

*Like most shorebirds, the black skimmer lays its eggs in groups of four*

against three older brothers and sisters, one of which will be three days its senior.

A skimmer chick is not very much unlike that of a gull or tern. In fact, if one saw one without knowing its parents, it might be impossible to identify. This difficulty would be due to the simple reason that the bill does not have the characteristics of the adult bird's. Both of the skimmer chick's mandibles meet at their tips. Scientists say that this is a case where "ontogeny recapitulates phylogeny." Thus the history of the individual recapitulates the history of the race, or the growth of this young skimmer from the first day of its downy stage to adulthood repeats the development of the skimmer from the more common type of bird to the specialized creature that it is today.

Not so far back in geologic time the skimmer and tern were probably alike; at least, they had a common ancestor. Their mandibles were of equal length. They fed alike, probably by plunging into the water for fishes. Then, for some inexplicable reason, one bird or group of birds began to feed as do our present-day skimmers and through adaptation developed a new type of bill, presumably to go with the habit. But each chick reared resembled the chicks of its ancestors and it was only when it began to feed in its own particular way that its specialized bill appeared (See under Adaptations of Birds).

Unless you are familiar with the habits of the black skimmer, Cardwell Island would not impress you as being an ideal nursery. The sand is exceedingly fine and shifts with the slightest breeze. An impression made by the human foot is covered within a few hours. There is no shade save that offered by pieces of driftwood jutting out of the sand, small plants, and clumps of grasses. Then, too, the more or less level surface of the beach easily absorbs the heat from the sun's rays and makes it painful to touch with one's hand. Nevertheless the young skimmer is well adapted to the vicissitudes of this coastal environment. To it the restless sand is an advantage, a means of protection. When left in the nest while its parents are in search of food, the sand gathers over its yellowish down, thus helping it to match all the more the earth of similar coloration on which it is confined. Sometimes the drifting wind-blown sand covers it over, and its tiny body is fitted neatly in a mold of sand with just its head, which it keeps shaking frequently, showing above it. Not uncommonly the chick hastens its own inundation by scratching out sand from beneath itself. Ordinarily the heat of the sand does not seem to annoy the chick. At times, however, it becomes so excessive that it can no longer endure it. Instinctively it heads for any available shade.

Generally the skimmer chick is well cared for by both parents. They bring it food, arriving at the nestside with small fishes held crosswise in their mouths. They take turns in brooding the chick, thus providing the protection from the heat of the day and the cool night air. If the chick happens to be the youngest in the family, it is sometimes at a disadvantage in getting its share of the food, since its brothers and sisters, stronger by age, push it aside when food is brought to them. But food comes often and there are times when the chick's great hunger makes up for what it does not possess in strength.

It is not long before the skimmer chick becomes a pin-feathered juvenile. Its wings grow enormously, seeming, once in a while, to get ahead of the relative growth of its body. When it stretches out its wings and waves them against the wind to gain strength, they appear far out of proportion to the chick's small body. But it is essential that they reach their full size as soon as possible, for the security provided by flight is needed by the growing youngster. Gradually the lower mandible of the chick becomes noticeably larger and more bladelike and begins to protrude beyond the upper

*A black skimmer incubates its eggs in a shallow depression scooped in the sand*

one. The plumage that develops is a mixture of grays and whites and blacks. There are no brilliant colors in the chick's feet and bill as yet. It will be at least a year before the young skimmer can don the robes of maturity.

To us, a skimmer's youth is the carefree one of storybooks. Protected on this isolated isle from the usual dangers that beset young birds on the mainland, its expectancy of life seems assured. At first the beach is its to roam, though it prefers only the neighborhood of the colony. The vigorous breakers and the mirrored tidal pools seem to fascinate the chick. One day it wades into the water, spies a small fish, strikes at it clumsily, fails to catch it, and returns hungry to its parents which are still coming back with food. On a later day the chick spreads its wings in a stiff breeze and finds itself lifted upward. It must be a delightful sensation. It alights and does it again. Soon it is flying everywhere, but particularly over shallow water. Instinctively the young skimmer flies low. It seems a part of it to open its mouth and cleave the water with its beak. It misjudges the scant depth and the tip of its beak strikes bottom, snapping its head beneath it suddenly. The next time it may cut through a wave too high for it and the wave breaks over its head. But give the skimmer time! Experience will teach it how to use this modification with greater dexterity.

By fall the sea-covered parts of the world belong to this youthful skimmer. Nevertheless, it frequents only the shores of the Caribbean Sea. It is a member of a flock of old and young skimmers. During the day it loiters on sandbars and wades and dabbles idly in shoal water. In the dusk it cleaves the water along the shores—one of a host of graceful shadows. —O.S.P., Jr.

# SKINK

Skinks are lizards of the family Scincidae. They comprise a very large group of species of worldwide distribution. There are about 12 species in the United States and Canada; some authorities list up to 20 species. All of them have conical heads, rounded bodies, and long and tapering tails. Their bodies are completely covered with smooth scales of uniform size which are larger and heavier on the head. The legs are short, and skinks, while able to scamper quickly, cannot rise on the hind legs and run as some other lizards can.

Most skinks are burrowers, spending much of their lives underground. The long tail helps them to gain leverage against solid objects in the soil as they force the heavily plated head through sand or loam. In some species that rarely leave their burrows, the eyes are very small, and the legs are degenerate. This description fits the sand skink, *Neoseps reynoldsi*, of eastern Florida, which has very small legs with only one digit on the forefeet and two on the rear ones.

Only one of the skinks in North America has a window in the lower eyelids, through which it may see when its eyes

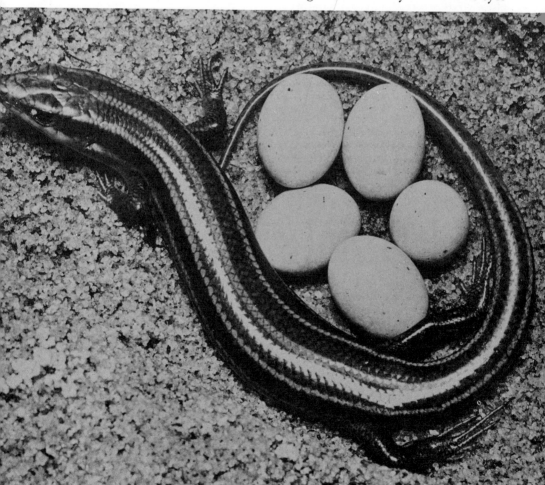

*Unlike most lizards, the female five-lined skink broods her eggs for six or seven weeks until they hatch*

are closed. Transparent scales protect its eyes as this reptile burrows, with the lower lid firmly clamped against the upper one. This is the little ground skink, or brown skink, *Lygosoma laterale*. It lives in the eastern and southeastern portion of the United States from New Jersey to the Florida Keys and west to eastern Kansas and central Texas. The slender body is about two inches long, and the tail may be as long or longer than the body.

All skinks are able to break off the tail when struggling with a captor. The detached tail twists and wriggles vigorously, often inducing the predator to concentrate upon it while the rest of the skink hurries off (*See under Reptile*).
—G.B.S.

*Recommended Reading*

**Amphibians and Reptiles of Western North America**—Robert C. Stebbins. McGraw-Hill, New York. **Handbook of Lizards: Lizards of the United States and Canada**—Hobart M. Smith. Comstock Publishing Company, Ithaca, New York. **The Natural History of North American Amphibians and Reptiles**—J. A. Oliver. D. Van Nostrand Company, Princeton, New Jersey.

**Five-lined Skink**
**Other Common Names**—Skink
**Scientific Name**— *Eumeces fasciatus*
**Family**—Scincidae (skinks)
**Order**—Squamata
**Size**—Length, 5 to 7½ inches
**Range**—Southern New England south to northern Florida, west to Wisconsin and eastern Texas. Also locally distributed in Iowa, Minnesota, northern Michigan, and South Dakota

The five-lined skink courts and mates in early spring. The eggs are laid, after a gestation period of six or seven weeks, in rotten logs or in loose soil several inches below the surface. Egg-laying is usually from early July to late August or possibly into early September. Clutches of eggs number 2 to 18; smaller clutches are laid by smaller females; larger clutches by larger females. The five-lined skink hibernates during the winter in rotten logs or in the ground. It usually feeds upon spiders, small insects, insect larvae, and earthworms.
—J.K.T.

*The five-lined skink grows a new, shorter tail if its original one is broken off*

*The skua, a large gull-like bird, lives in the sea and is seldom seen near land*

## SKUA

**Other Common Names**—Sea hawk
**Scientific Name**—*Catharacta skua*
**Family**—Stercorariidae (jaegers and skuas)
**Order**—Charadriiformes
**Size**—Length, 21 inches
**Range**—Breeds on islands off the coast of Europe and in the Antarctic; northern population winters at sea south to New England

Skuas look like large, brown gulls. Their tails are shorter than those of the average gulls, and are square cut. The brown plumage of the back contrasts strongly with the white bases of the primary feathers.

Skuas are strong, sturdy predators. They nest near other colonial seabirds and exact a toll of eggs and nestlings. They also rob other birds of captured food, forcing them to disgorge it. Any dead animal matter is acceptable, including refuse from fishing boats and whale factory ships.

The flight of the skua is fast, the broad wings moving in deep and rapid strokes, giving the bird more the appearance of a hawk than that of a gull. It does not dive into the water, but drops to the surface and swims.

Seldom seen near land except near the breeding colonies, skuas are birds of the open sea.                    —G.B.S.

# SKUNK

There are six species of skunks that live within the United States — the eastern spotted skunk, or civet, *Spilogale putorius;* the striped skunk, *Mephitis mephitis;* the hog-nosed skunk, *Conepatus mesoleucus;* the eastern hog-nosed skunk, *Conepatus leuconotus;* the western spotted skunk, *Spilogale gracilis;* and the hooded skunk, *Mephitis macroura,* that enters partway into extreme southern California in the southwestern United States from Baja California. Skunks are classified in the order Carnivora, and family Mustelidae. (*See under Mammal*). In North America the family includes, besides the skunks, the weasels, minks, fishers, martens, wolverines, badgers, and otters. Although they range into South America, skunks are North American animals known only from the western hemisphere. They are especially well known for their well-developed anal scent glands. All species are black-furred with various stripes or spots of white, depending on the species and the markings of the individual skunks, which can vary considerably. As in most mustelids, the males are larger than the females. —J.K.T.

## Striped Skunk
**Other Common Names** — Common skunk
**Scientific Name** — *Mephitis mephitis*
**Family** — Mustilidae (weasels, skunks, and allies)
**Order** — Carnivora
**Size** — Male: body length, 24 to 30 inches; tail, 7 to 9 inches; height at shoulder, 7 to 8 inches; weight, 4 to 10 pounds. Females about one-fifth smaller
**Range** — Southern Canada (north in Alberta, British Columbia, and Saskatchewan) south through all of the United States to northern Mexico, excluding Baja California

Of all the small mammals that inhabit our open fields and brushy cutover lands, one of the most interesting and useful is the striped skunk, *Mephitis mephitis.* A native of every state and all of southern Canada, the striped skunk is virtually everybody's neighbor. It is especially well known to country people and villagers for it often makes its home under farm buildings or beneath sheds on the outskirts of small towns. Probably almost everyone has heard of the skunk and knows something about its unique means of defense, concerning which we shall say more later, but perhaps comparatively few persons appreciate the great service it renders our farms and gardens every day as it goes about its business of eating.

The skunk is a capacious mousetrap. The farmer is wise who encourages these animals to hunt mice in his barn by setting out an enticing saucer or two of milk for the skunks to find as they prowl about after dark. Insects also form a large part of their diet. Skunks are heavy eaters and during the summer they eat hordes of crickets and grasshoppers that cause so much havoc in the grainfields. The young insects, such as cutworms or other larvae, that chew the stems and leaves of our garden plants, are particularly relished by skunks. Many plants are spared destruction by insects as the result of the nocturnal feeding of a family of skunks. In the cool of the evening, after the dew has fallen, many insects, particularly those that feed on plants, become sluggish and inactive. These are easily scooped up and devoured by skunks. It was because of their usefulness as consumers of insects that are destructive to hop plants that skunks became the first furbearers in New York State to win legislation for their protection.

Of course the skunk has a liking for hen's eggs and young chickens and for the eggs and young of ground birds too, occasionally adding these to its diet when they are easily available. Depredations of this sort, however, are far outweighed by the quantities of insects and mice they devour. Perhaps a farmer might consider the loss of a few chicks or eggs as a paycheck to the skunk for

*Striped skunks live in almost any kind of habitat where they are active at dusk and after dark*

its services. Better yet, with a snug, well-built hen house, the farmer need not fear losses of this kind.

The skunk is a handsome animal, with a black suit of silky fur variously marked with white. A usual pattern for the striped skunk is black with a white nose and cap, and two white stripes on the back meeting at the neck to form a V. The plumelike tail is a mixture of long black-and-white hairs, and has a conspicuous white tip. An attractive cousin is the little spotted skunk. It is commonly called civet cat in the fur trade, and lives in scattered areas of the southern, central, and western United States. It has a very striking mottled coat. Another cousin, the hog-nosed skunk of Arizona and New Mexico, has the back, top of head, and upper side of the tail all white. Skunk pelts have long been used in the fur trade. Alaska sable, black marten, tipped skunk, and marten are commercial names for natural or dyed skunk fur.

Skunks belong to a very important family of furbearers that contributes the major share of American fur pelts to the world market. This is the weasel family, the Mustelidae, to which the weasel, marten, fisher, mink, otter, skunk, wolverine, and badger belong. Like many forms of wildlife for which commercial use has been found, several members of this famous family have been seriously reduced in number through excessive trapping carried on without regard to maintaining an adequate breeding stock.

The striped skunk, often locally called wood pussy, is actually about the size of a house cat, but with a proportionately smaller head, stockier body, shorter legs, and a bushy tail. In movement it does not in the least resemble the cat, which runs swiftly about on the tips of its toes, digitigrade. The skunk walks about semiplantigrade, that is, with its heels on the ground as well as its toes, and with both palms and fingers bearing its weight. The hind foot of a

*The spotted skunk is the smallest North American skunk and has white spots on its head and several white stripes along its body*

skunk makes a footprint very much like that of a human baby. Plantigrade animals must necessarily move more slowly than those such as cats, dogs, and deer, which travel on their toes, and even among the plantigrades the skunk seems exceedingly deliberate.

A skunk has no need to hurry in order to capture food. Its forefeet, equipped with long, thick, almost straight claws for digging out the shallow burrows of mice, ripping apart old rotten logs, and digging in the sand for turtle eggs, means that food can be obtained without it giving chase. Insects are captured by it at night when too cool to move quickly; baby mice are consumed in their nests, where an adult mouse may also be surprised.

Speed is just as unnecessary to the skunk when it comes to escaping from its enemies. Probably the skunk's worst enemy is the great horned owl. Flying silently with its soft-tipped wings, the owl pounces on the skunk from above. Swiftness would be of little help to a skunk in evading this attack from the air at night. Other potential enemies, such as the dog and fox, will usually,

after a little experience, leave the skunk alone. Skunks are as plainly marked in black and white as a railroad crossing, and easily recognized even in the dark.

The skunk carries a very effective and potent defense weapon which enables it to go through life in so unhurried a fashion. At the base of the tail and entirely separate from the organs of excretion are two scent glands. Each is equipped with a nozzle and muscular attachment capable of ejecting a spray of evil-smelling liquid of a penetrating character for a distance of several feet. Contrary to popular belief, it is the liquid that smells—not the skunk. An exceptionally clean little animal, the skunk ordinarily has no odor about it at all. The liquid is used only in self defense and even then the skunk obligingly gives ample warning of its intentions. When annoyed it raises its tail to a vertical position. If further annoyed it stamps its paws. Then woe to the creature, man or beast, that has failed to heed these danger signals! An instant later the tail is thrust forward over the back, the hind end is directed toward the source of annoyance, and the spray is ejected.

This effective defense mechanism very probably has something to do with the fact that the skunk lacks the wildness of most of our native mammals. It is easily tamed and because of its interesting and useful habits makes an amusing and valuable neighbor. Moreover, it is not always necessary to take the initiative in attracting a skunk. It may of its own accord take up its abode in one's yard. A nook beneath the barn or woodshed makes an admirable skunk den, and with garden insects nearby and mice in the barn, the environment is most propitious for raising a family. Little skunks, usually six or eight to a litter, are born sometime between April and June. Like kittens, they are blind at birth and take considerable time to mature. The nursery is lined with a thick bed of leaves and grass—a comfortable home for the little skunks, which do not begin to venture outside until they are about six weeks old.

In the wild, an old woodchuck burrow is frequently appropriated by the striped skunk as a den. Aside from farm buildings and the outskirts of small towns, the usual habitats are open fields, cutover woodlands, brushy places, and wet pastures. In these places there is always an abundance of crickets and grasshoppers during the summer, and mouse nests are plentiful too. Along sandy stream banks are nests of turtle eggs. These are greatly relished by skunks and their consumption in some areas serves as a valuable control over the numbers of snapping turtles.

Herein lies an interesting story in interrelationship. Snappers eat a great many fish and young ducks. When snappers are plentiful, fish and ducks are scarce; when snappers are few, the numbers of fish and waterfowl increase. Because skunks are fond of snapping turtle eggs and raid the sand banks where snappers have laid large quantities of their eggs, there are few snapping turtles where skunks are abundant, and consequently there are more fish and more waterfowl. Thus each of these animals serves to check the number of animals upon which it preys and the numbers of these in turn determine the numbers of their enemies that can remain in the area to feed on them. Interrelationships of this sort, and broadened to include relations between the plants, animals, soil, and water of a community, constitute a sort of natural balance—"the balance of nature." (See Balance of Nature; and under Wildlife: The Wildlife Community). It is in the role of insect-eater, however, that the skunk fits most effectively into this general balance of nature. Skunks are said to destroy more insects than all the other kinds of mammals put together.

Its industry, plus a big appetite, add considerably to the skunk's weight. By fall, there is usually a thick layer of fat beneath the skin. In the northern part of the range, this serves both as a warm blanket and as a food supply for the cold season. Although generally, skunks are active every month in the year, during periods of deep snow and excessive cold they lie snugly in their dens in winter sleep. They are one of the seven mammals that hibernate (see Hibernation) in southern Canada; the other six are the bat, bear, jumping mouse, woodchuck, chipmunk, and raccoon. To quote Ernest Thompson Seton:

"The bat and the bear, they never care
What winter winds may blow,
The jumping mouse in its cozy house
Is safe from ice and snow.
The chipmunk and the woodchuck,
The skunk that's slow but sure,
The ringed raccoon who hates the moon,
Have found for cold the cure."

The skunk's winter sleep, however, is not a deep one and on warm days it ventures forth in search of some unwary mouse, and thus its tracks are frequently found in the snow.          —W.E.S.

Recommended Reading

American Mammals—Stone & Cram. Doubleday, Doran & Company, Inc., New York.

**Field Book of North American Mammals** – H. E. Anthony. G. P. Putnam's Sons, New York.

**Lives of Game Animals** – Ernest Thompson Seton. Charles T. Bradford Company, Boston.

**Mammals of Eastern United States** – W. J. Hamilton, Jr. Comstock Publishing Company, Ithaca, New York.

**Mammals of North America** – Victor H. Cahalane. The Macmillan Company, New York.

**Spring and Summer Activities of the Dusky Skunk in Captivity** – William T. Shaw and K. F. Chamberlain. New York State Museum, Handbook 4, Albany, New York.

## SLEET (*See under Frost*)

## SLOTH

The sloths—the two-toed, *Choloepus hoffmanni*, and the three-toed, *Bradypus griseus*—are tropical American mammals that live nowhere else in the world but in the western hemisphere. They are limited to the forests of Central and South America. Both species are tree-dwelling herbivores that are active at night (nocturnal) and are usually solitary. Sloths hang by their claws, suspended from tree branches, with their backs to the ground. They move slowly along tree branches by a "hand-over-hand" locomotion, using all four legs and feet. The three-toed sloth has a short tail, but the two-toed species is tailless.
— J.K.T.

**Three-toed Sloth**
**Other Common Names** – Pedro lingero
**Scientific Name** – *Bradypus griseus*
**Family** – Bradypodidae (sloths)
**Order** – Edentata
**Size** – Body length, 23 to 26½ inches; tail, 2½ to 3 inches; weight, up to 10 pounds
**Range** – Eastern Honduras south through tropical South America

**Two-toed Sloth**
**Other Common Names** – None
**Scientific Name** – *Choloepus hoffmanni*
**Family** – Bradypodidae (sloths)
**Order** – Edentata
**Size** – Body length, 24 to 25½ inches; weight, up to 12 pounds

**Range** – Central Nicaragua south through tropical South America

### "Slowpoke" of the American Tropics

Someone has commented that sloths are deliberate and cautious rather than lazy. Alexander Skutch, an ornithologist living in Costa Rica, estimated that the three-toed sloth may take as much as 30 minutes to chew a large cecropia leaf, a compound leaf comparable in size to one of the large palmate leaves like the horse chestnut of the eastern United States.

Both the two-toed and the three-toed sloths are at home in trees and can climb swiftly. When one observer in Panama released a captive two-toed sloth at the base of a cecropia tree in the village of Pedro Miguel it hitched up the trunk whose circumference was at least twice that of the sloth's outstretched forearms.

On the ground sloths are awkward and slow; both kinds swim. In British Guiana, the late William Beebe, an American naturalist, marked a three-toed sloth and later recovered it after it had swum a mile-wide river. He timed the swimming speed of this sloth at the rate of 65 feet a minute. By comparison with its slow rate of movement over bare ground, the three-toed moves much more rapidly in the water.

Few, if any, zoos have been able to keep the three-toed sloth alive. Its diet is commonly thought to be leaves of the cecropia. W. M. Mann, the former director of the National Zoological Park at Washington, wrote as follows of the problem of keeping this species alive. ". . . I started out once from British Guiana with an even dozen of them. The Director General of Agriculture wired ahead to various islands so each stop we made on the way to New York I was met by the local agriculture man and a bunch of fresh cecropia leaves. Only one of the animals lived to reach Washington and it died the following day." Once a three-toed sloth lived briefly at the Bronx Zoo, in New York.

*High in a tropical cecropia tree, a three-toed sloth takes 30 minutes to chew each leaf*

Sloths live only in tropical America from the Amazon River north through Central America. In the Panama Canal Zone, the ranges of the two-toed and the three-toed overlap, just as do those of the howler monkey and the white-faced, or capuchin, monkey (*See under Monkey*). The two species of sloths apparently do not conflict in their feeding requirements.

The two-toed eats a wide variety of plants, but the three-toed is thought to be dependent on the leaves of the cecropia tree. These trees are distinctive of the New World tropics, but they are not typically a tree of the dense forest. Many sloths are found in the so-called jungle or tropical rain forest, but Paul Swanson,

a naturalist in Panama during World War II, caught most of his specimens in the large grassy meadows or savannas around La Chorrera, Panama. He also found three sloths that had been run over by cars along the highway. Sloths tend to move across these tropical meadows in order to get from one clump of cecropias to another.

Cecropia trees are especially common in the Canal Zone, on cutover land. This suggests that sloths are more abundant *since man came to the jungle* than before, because with more disturbance of the dense forest, more cecropias grow and therefore provide much more food for three-toed sloths.

*The two-toed sloth (above) has two claws on its front feet; while the three-toed sloth (below) has three. Both species spend much of their lives in trees*

Structurally, the two sloths are easily distinguished. A comparison will show the three-toed sloth, with its three claws on each front foot, in contrast to the two claws of its cousin. The three-toed sloth has hair to the base of its claws, but the two-toed sloth has elongated hairless "palms." The three-toed sloth has a rather pious mien, whereas the two-toed seems to have a "chip-on-the shoulder" air. The incomplete black mask through the eyes of the three-toed increases its harmless appearance.

Both species are covered with a mat of extremely long hair which gives them a deceptively heavy appearance. Though about as big as a beaver, the weight of a sloth is not nearly so great. No living sloth is larger than a medium-sized dog (about 26 to 27 inches long) and they have only a stub of a tail.

It is interesting that the longest hair starts on the abdomen and sweeps around and over the back. Since the sloth is generally in an inverted position while traveling along under a jungle limb, this arrangement of hair permits effective shedding of rainfall.

Two-toed sloths have hair that is grooved, thus providing crevices in which minute plants live. These green plants obtain protection and suitable environment for their needs; the sloth benefits from the camouflage derived from the green color which varies from gray-green in the dry season to a deep green when the jungle is emerald green during the wet season. The relationship between sloth and green algae is thus mutually satisfactory. A similar relationship exists between the three-toed sloth and algae, though the hairs are not grooved but possess tiny cracks crosswise on the hairs, in which the algae spend their lives. Interestingly, the species of algae that live upon the two animals are different, although both species belong to the genus *Pleurococcus* and must have evolved independently in the slightly different crevices in the hairs of the two kinds of sloths.

The dense hair of the sloth makes it possible for it to browse in the cecropias unharmed by the stinging azteca ants. Algae in the cracks or grooves of the hairs also provide for small moths which, in their larval stage, subsist upon these minute green plants. The moths do not appear to chew on the hair itself.

Both kinds of sloths have but one young at birth and the mother carries it until the young one is well grown. The immature sloth may cling to the mother as if she were a tree limb, or it may ride on the breast of the mother as she moves in an inverted position. Probably it is weaned gradually as it strays away from its mother in attempting to browse on its own.

Although two-toed sloths are apathetic, they use every means at their command to intimidate a potential enemy. Their blocky build, the gaping, hissing mouth, and the powerfully muscled biceps and sharp claws are formidable in action. Although they stoutly resist capture and handling they live for only short periods in captivity.

The untamable nature of a recently captured two-toed sloth is reminiscent of the behavior of an adult badger of the western United States (*See Badger*). Young badgers may be tamed and, so may young sloths, to a degree, while they live. For example, a female baby two-toed sloth captured by Robert Enders made a pet of sorts when taken to Swarthmore Pennsylvania. Regarding her defense behavior, Enders wrote in the *Journal of Mammalogy* that restricting her movements aroused her anger. She hissed, used her claws and attempted to bite, but her anger was short-lived. She did not appear to recognize individual persons, but would attach herself to the clothing of friend or stranger, presumably for warmth.

Adult sloths in the tropics may have relatively few enemies, but the odds are seemingly against them ever becoming adults. Once they do, statistics may favor their survival. The sloths have their enemies, of which man is one. Leo Miller, who explored South America with former President Theodore Roosevelt, wrote that some of the natives find the flesh much to their liking.

Among the possible enemies of the sloth are the tree-climbing boas, the jaguar, cougar, and the harpy eagle. On January 8, 1947, an observer on Barro Colorado Island, Panama Canal Zone (*see under Monkey*), saw a harpy eagle flash down through the green jungle roof to seize a large toucan and eat it. The piercing wail of the doomed animal was symbolic of its helplessness. A young sloth might be just as helpless. A. Hyatt-Verrill, the ethnologist, in his book on Panama experiences, reported that the natives call the harpy a sloth eagle. He writes that he was an eyewitness to a harpy eagle swooping down through the jungle to seize a sloth. He collected the eagle and disposed of the mutilated body of the sloth. Frank Chapman saw a young cougar on Barro Colorado Island eating a three-toed sloth.

The sloth has some protection against enemies. It has postures in which it "freezes" for long periods of time, and its algal cover renders it so inconspicuous that in the daytime it might resemble a termite nest. The dozen hooked claws of the three-toed, or even the 10 hooks of the two-toed (the two-toed sloth has 2 hooks on its forefeet and 3 on its hind feet), provide a tenacious grip on tree branches, for it is more than likely, though not always, in its inverted position when danger threatens. Thus the traditional "above-the-branch predator," such as the jungle cats or the eagle, have difficulty in getting to the sloth.

Sloths have a four-layer inner defense of 20 pairs of flat ribs, half again as many pairs as most other mammals, including the arboreal monkeys. Also, it has a hide notoriously hard to penetrate with arrows, and a coat of two distinct layers, the inner soft fur and the long outer guard hairs. This amazingly tough hide probably protects the sloth while swimming in waters infested by the piranha (a fierce carnivorous fish), crocodiles, and electric eels.

All in all both species of sloths are well adapted for survival in the jungle; nevertheless, it is doubtful that anyone has studied them well enough to know the particular niche into which each of the two species fit.

There is need for some enterprising young naturalist, who is interested in tropical animals, to make a study of sloths. He could doubtless use the facilities of the Barro Colorado Island naturalists' paradise for at least part of his studies. He might learn much from the Martinique Negroes as to where they find the two kinds of sloths, and he would want to make observations around the grassy savannas in the vicinity of the Panama Canal Zone where Paul Swanson made some of his observations. This study could be an intriguing and fruitful investigation. There is still much to be learned about the behavior of sloths, their voice, courtship, and personality.
—C.W.Q.

**SLUG** (*See under Snails and Slugs*)

**SMELT**
**American Smelt**
**Other Common Names**—Saltwater smelt
**Scientific Name**—*Osmerus mordax*
**Family**—Osmeridae (smelts)
**Order**—Clupeiformes
**Size**—Length, to 14 inches
**Range**—In both salt and fresh water of the Atlantic Coast area from Labrador to Virginia. Landlocked in freshwater lakes in Canada, Maine, New York, and New Hampshire. Artificially introduced into the Great Lakes

The American smelt's body is only about one-fifth as deep as it is long. Its head is long and pointed with a large mouth and fairly small eyes. There are large, fanglike teeth on the smelt's tongue. There is one well-developed dor-

*The American smelt has been greatly reduced in numbers by water pollution and the construction of dams*

sal fin followed by a small adipose (fatty) fin on the back.

The American smelt's back is transparent olive to bottle-green. The sides are lighter with a horizontal silver band. The belly is silvery.

This fish is one of several that spend most of their lives in the ocean but swim up into rivers to spawn. Smelts are fine food fishes, but their number has been reduced greatly by man's careless handling of nature. Water pollution and dams and various other construction projects have in many cases cut the fishes off from or, worse, completely destroyed their spawning places.

A few other smelts include the pond smelt, *Hypomesus olidus,* the Arctic smelt, *Osmerus dentex,* and the Sacramento smelt, *Spirinchus thaleichthys.*
—M.R.

**SMUT** (*See under Fungus*)

**SNAIL**

Snails are classified in a general group of invertebrate animals known as mollusks (phylum Mollusca). The name means *soft-bodied,* and the group includes, besides snails, the chitons, bivalves (*see Bivalve*), octopuses, and squids. Among the mollusks (*see Mollusk*), the snails are in the class Gastropoda (*See Gastropod*). Two subclasses in the gastropoda include the so-called marine snails; a third subclass includes the freshwater snails and land snails.

The most obvious feature of a snail is its spiral shell, which it manufactures from calcium, carbon, and oxygen extracted from its food. This compound is deposited by the mantle, the fleshy envelope that surrounds its other organs. In the slugs the shell is entirely lacking.

A marine snail breathes underwater through a ctenidium (the characteristic gastropod gill) whereas land snails and those that live in fresh water breathe air by means of a lung. The lung is the vascular wall of the mantle cavity. Though the greater part of their class (Gastropoda, a division of the phylum Mollusca) are marine, this small land and freshwater group will drown if immersed under water for too long (*See under Pond*).

The head of a snail has two pairs of tentacles, with simple eyes on the second pair. The mouth is underneath; it is equipped with a jaw and a coiled rod of tissue (radula) studded with teeth. The foot is the large muscle on which a snail travels over the ground or other surfaces.

Land snails are generally vegetarian. They are also hermaphroditic, each individual bearing both male and female glands.

The univalves, the marine snails (mollusks with one coiled shell), are also in the class Gastropoda. Some typical marine snails are moon shells, periwinkles, conchs, cowries, and whelks. The sea slugs and sea butterflies are also gastropods, but have evolved away from the shell-forming characteristic.

The general gastropod body consists of a mantle, a fleshy tissue that surrounds the rest of the body and that secretes the material of the shell; a head with eye stalks and feelers; a mouth with a rasping organ called a radula; a mass of visceral organs situated farther back in the shell; and a fleshy projection called a foot, sometimes provided with a hard operculum, on which the animal moves over the bottom.

The entire internal anatomy of the gastropods is twisted to conform with the coiling of the shell (*See discussion under Mollusk*). The members of paired organs (kidneys, gills, heart chambers) on the left side are large and functional, while those on the right are usually degenerate or missing.

Most marine snails are vegetarian, but some, such as the whelks and some of the conchs, are carnivorous. There are about 50,000 species within the class.
—G.B.S.

### Habits of Some Land Snails

It is literally true that no matter where one finds himself in America he will never be very far away from some form of land snails. Their presence may be completely unsuspected, but if one knows where to look and what to look for, land snails can be found in every state in the Union and probably in every county of each state. Whether one is in the lowlands of coastal plains, the high reaches

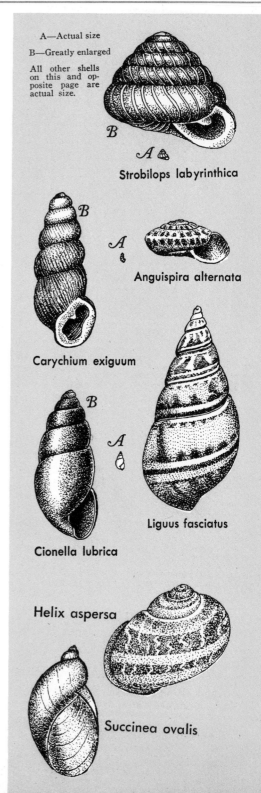

A—Actual size

B—Greatly enlarged

All other shells on this and opposite page are actual size.

Strobilops labyrinthica

Anguispira alternata

Carychium exiguum

Liguus fasciatus

Cionella lubrica

Helix aspersa

Succinea ovalis

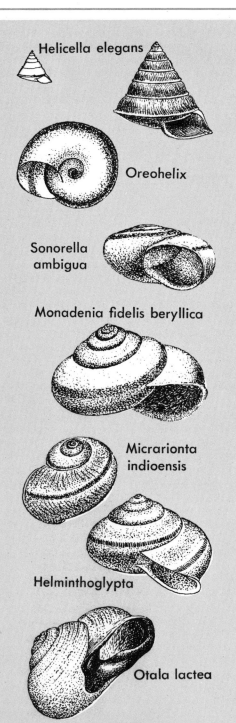

Helicella elegans

Oreohelix

Sonorella ambigua

Monadenia fidelis beryllica

Micrarionta indioensis

Helminthoglypta

Otala lactea

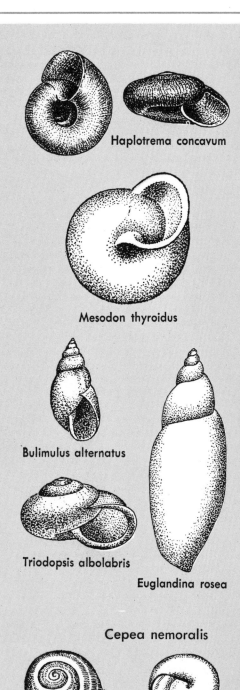

Haplotrema concavum

Mesodon thyroidus

Bulimulus alternatus

Triodopsis albolabris

Euglandina rosea

Cepea nemoralis

of mountain peaks, the cactus covered wastes of deserts or even in teeming cities, one can always be sure that somewhere not far away land snails exist and even flourish.

The forests of the eastern United States, especially the mountains of Georgia, Tennessee, Alabama, and the two Carolinas simply swarm with land snails of various sizes, shapes, and habits. It is true that they are not very large nor very showy. The larger ones are up to 1½ inches in diameter, and about ¾ inches high, whereas the smaller ones are minute points from 1½ to 4 millimeters in size. Most of them are dull brown or buff in color, a few are pleasingly shiny, but, excepting the Florida tree snails, they have no vivid colors such as one sees in sea shells. It is a pity that these practically omnipresent little creatures are not better known, but there is some satisfaction in noticing that the number of people seriously interested in them is steadily increasing.

The phylum Mollusca, to which the land snails belong, contains the second largest number of all animals, and is outnumbered only by insects and their relatives. And by far the largest number live in the sea. Like many creatures of the land that ultimately stem from sea-dwelling ancestors, the land snails need constant supplies of moisture to continue to be active, or even to survive. Once a famous zoologist was heard to protest that the term "land animals" is a biological misnomer, since all living creatures are actually sea animals that carry the true environment of all life, the salt sea, around with them like ambulating tanks of varying degrees of efficiency. If this is so, then the tank of the land snails is very defective.

If the immediate environment is too dry, snails cease their activity and retire into their shells where they live in suspended animation until moisture returns to the air. But they will drown rather quickly in a superabundance of water. For these reasons snails must be looked for in shady areas that are damp but not wet, such as dank forest dells and glades that have a thick ground cover of rotting leaves. They also live on the well shaded, foliage-covered sides of calcareous or schist cliffs where they cling under the rock overhangs. In cities they live in dank cellars or under moisture conserving debris in empty lots. For some reason they are sparse in pine forests, and seem to prefer good stands of hardwood oaks and maples.

Once a train was held up in the open spaces of Kansas and a snail collecting passenger, to while away the waiting time, reconnoitered the small broken stones on the railroad bed. There he found amazingly large quantities of small mollusks. Since the sun is a moisture absorber, land snails are largely active at night and rarely venture forth when the sun is shining. However, cloudy mornings that follow a rainy night will sometimes lure them forth to feed.

Snails that inhabit desert regions — and, surprisingly, many species are found nowhere else — have developed remarkable powers of hibernation (better *estivation* since it is the searing summer suns they seek to avoid, rather than the killing frosts of winter). They are active only during infrequent desert rains (*See under Desert*). Otherwise, occasionally for years at a stretch, they hide in the deep crevices of rocky talus slopes. No one has actually taken the trouble to find out just how long these desert snails can go without eating or drinking, but there is a record of a desert snail collected in Egypt in the 1850's. The animal was so dormant that it was supposed the shell was empty. In the museum manner of that time, it was pasted on a labelled card and mounted in a display case in the British Museum. Four years later an attendant noticed that the animal was coming out of its shell and was still very much alive. It was fed some cabbage leaves and, apparently none the worse for its long sleep, went about its interrupted life.

*Because of their nocturnal habits, many people are unfamiliar with the land snail*

The nocturnal and hibernating habits of our native land snails are one reason why many people, especially in the United States, are not aware of their existence. Another reason is their comparative lack of economic importance. They do not eat what we like, but subsist largely on woodland vegetation, usually when it is decaying, and on the minute mycelium of forest fungi. They contribute their tiny share to the endless circle of life and death by eating the rotting forest leaves and thus help to break them down to their simplest chemical essentials. In this manner they aid in keeping the forest ground relatively clear of fallen leaves which might otherwise pile up in impenetrable masses. Just what proportion of this type of work snails do in comparison with other organisms has never been determined. But it may be safely assumed that it is not very large.

Land snails form part of the diet of birds, frogs, toads, snakes, and small mammals like chipmunks, field mice, shrews, and moles. The snail collector frequently comes across fresh shells with broken spires, from which the soft parts have been extracted, the work most likely of hungry forest rodents. One finds eight to ten mutilated shells to every living one in good condition. Hence it can be seen that the human searcher is a good deal less skillful a hunter than his animal competitors. In England there are certain "feeding rocks," that birds use against which to bang snail shells till they break and the bird can get at the soft flesh within. The ground around these sacrificial boulders is strewn with fragments of broken shells.

In a moving picture called *Chico* one can see such an event actually taking place. A roadrunner, a southwestern bird of the cuckoo family, in this case seized

The rare and vanishing Everglades kite (above) feeds exclusively on the green snail, Pomacea paludosa (below). Although an aquatic species, the green snail has adaptations in its gill cavity that allow it to breathe air for short periods

a small, white, elevated shell (evidently of the Texas genus *Bulimulus*) in its long, pointed beak and hit it repeatedly against a boulder till it fell free of its calcareous cover. It seized the tiny morsel again, gave it a quick shake or two to free it of adhering bits of broken shell, and then swallowed it with an upward toss of the head.

Besides constituting the prey of animals, snails are also consumed by beetles. Some of these beetles of the subfamily *Cychrinae*, which live in the great Smoky Mountains of Tennessee and North Carolina, have their heads and mandibles elongated and specially constructed to be forced into the aperture of shells to get to the soft body within. Evidently snails are their main source of food. The only other animals that live largely or even entirely on snails are other snails — flesh-eating species that dine off their herbivorous relatives. These predatory mollusks belong to the genera *Haplotrema* and *Euglandina*. The former has a yellowish-green shell about three-quarters of an inch in diameter. It is quite flat. It lives in the forests wherever its victims, namely other snails, can be found. It moves quite rapidly for a snail and attacks its prey with most unsnail-like ferocity, forcing its slender body into the aperture of the food snail and consuming every morsel to the very tip. In the case of smaller snails it devours them entire, shell and all. *Euglandina* lives in the South, mainly in Florida. It has a high, stout, spindle-shaped shell, pinkish- or reddish-buff in color, and much the same ruthless habits as *Haplotrema*.

The interested reader might perhaps like to know some of the species of land snails that can be found in his neighborhood. The late Henry A. Pilsbry of the Academy of Natural Sciences of Philadelphia, who died at the age of ninety-four, of which seventy-five years were devoted to the science of malacology, wrote a monumental work in four large tomes on the land mollusca of the United States. In this work he described exactly 1,141 species of native land snails, and more are being discovered and named every year. Nevertheless it might be of some value to describe briefly the outstanding groups that can be found in the various sections of our country.

In the eastern part of the United States, the largest land snails belong either to the genus *Triodopsis* or *Mesodon*. Both genera belong to the exclusively American snail family Polygyridae. The two commonest and most widely spread species are the common forest snail, *Mesodon thyroidus*, and the white-lipped forest snail, *Triodopsis albolabris*. Both have depressed shells — not elevated like the Texan *Bulimulus* that went to feed the roadrunner. They are about three-quarters of an inch high and one inch in diameter. The size, however, varies greatly in different specimens, depending upon the type of habitat in which it is found. Snails are usually smaller when they live in the largely granitic areas of lower New York because of the absence of calcium carbonate to build their shells. In the calcium-rich areas of upper New York and the Midwest the same species grow larger and heavier shells.

Both *Triodopsis albolabris* and *Mesodon thyroidus* live everywhere in the eastern part of North America as far west as the Mississippi River and, at least with *Mesodon*, as far south as northern Florida. In the region of the Great Smoky Mountains and Mt. Mitchell live many relatives of these snails. There can be found *Mesodon chilhoweensis*, called the "Queen of the Mesodons" because of its large size and impressive appearance. Incidentally, it could just as well be called the "King of the Mesodons," for almost all our land snails, big and little, are hermaphroditic. This, of course, gives them a great advantage in the struggle to survive on land, since every individual is an egg-bearer — there are no useless male drones. Many of the *Mesodons* in the Great Smokies are smaller than *thy-*

roidus, some are a good deal larger, but all more or less resemble one another. There too is the metropolis of the interesting genus *Stenotrema*. These are small, less than one-half inch in diameter, and have rounded shells like elliptical druggist's pills. They have a narrow mouth (hence its name, which in Greek means *narrow aperture*) that is usually guarded by a strong, white, shelly ridge.

In the eastern part of the nation we also find the alternate forest snail, *Anguispira alternata*, with a very pretty shell covered with dull reddish flame markings. It is about the size of *Mesodon*, but it never develops a reflected lip about the aperture even when it is fully grown. It has the same habits as the others but tends to be less solitary and lives in sizeable colonies. It is found more frequently in city lots than the other two. In the Greenwood Cemetery in Brooklyn lives a brightly colored subspecies of this snail called *A. alternata fergusoni*. It was named *fergusoni* for an enthusiastic collector by the name of Ferguson of the early 20th Century.

Although there is hardly room even to mention the name of the other snails that inhabit the eastern part of the continent, we must at least call attention to the tiny snails, from 1½ to 4 millimeters in size. They are found literally everywhere in suitable places. Most of our land shell species are of this diminutive size. They appear in many interesting shapes and colors. Some of them look like tiny insect pupae and hence are called *Pupillidae;* some look like truncated pine cones, for which reason they are called *Strobilops*, which is Greek for such an object; some are like tiny grains of rice, for example, *Carychium*.

For the most part the story of these tiny creatures is a mystery; very little is known about their life cycles, their habits, and their place in the economy of nature. When such a snail does get to be studied, surprising and important facts are discovered as in the case of *Cionella*,

the innocent vector of cattle disease. One can only wonder how many more such facts remain to be discovered in the life histories of the other tiny snails.

As one travels southward, the land snail fauna gradually changes. In southern Georgia and Florida, snails of the genus *Polygyra* begin to appear and become the dominant form. These are much smaller and flatter then *Mesodon* and *Triodopsis* and frequently consist of many narrow whorls, whence their very apt scientific name which means *many whorled*. Many Ploygyra species have the aperture obstructed by an amazing series of toothlike ridges and extensions that presumably serve to protect the soft parts from insect, chiefly beetle, attack. One species is called *Polygyra auriformis* because its aperture with its protecting extensions looks startlingly like a tiny human ear. Every unimproved lot in Miami, Florida, where plant debris has been allowed to accumulate has large numbers of some small polygyrid.

Traveling still farther south we reach the area of *Liguus*, the most beautiful land snail in America and one of the handsomest in the world. They live high up in trees, but descend to the ground to lay their eggs. During the dry season they estivate by attaching themselves to tree trunks with a slime that hardens to rocklike consistency. *Liguus* is a large snail, the largest in the United States, between two and three inches in height. It has an elevated shape like its related form the *Bulimulus* of Texas. The base color is a gleaming white like expensive porcelain. This is decorated with brown, orange, yellow, violet, and green bands of varying width. These bands, from Latin *ligo,* are the reason for its euphonious name. Many shells also have vivid flamelike markings. A collection of these snails is one of the most beautiful sights in natural history.

*Liguus,* a member of the widely distributed family Orthalicidae was originally an immigrant from Cuba, from whence it came sailing on floating tree branches impelled by the wild force of hurricane winds. When these were stranded on the keys and hammocks of southern Florida, the snail passengers disembarked. In the course of the centuries they developed into races of *Liguus* that have become characteristic for even such tiny localities as small, water-surrounded hammocks or islets in the Everglades. Many of these isolated snail populations have been given subspecific and varietal names. Some are so scarce that *Liguus* fanciers pay fat prices for coveted specimens. Destructive Everglade fires, the consequence of large-scale draining activities, have destroyed completely many of these beautiful local forms. Specimens of these vanished races, like rare stamps, command especially good prices.

The story is heard that occasionally unscrupulous collectors will come across a new race in some unexplored hammock. They collect all the specimens they possibly can and then set fire to the hammock, destroying the eggs and immature shells (as well as everything else). In this way they insure for themselves that their special *Liguus* race will remain scarce and expensive. We like to call this fact deliberately to the attention of people. It is comforting to know that with the recent establishment of Everglades National Park, *Liguus* will continue to thrive at least in part of its former range.

In Texas and elsewhere in the Southwest lives *Bulimulus* the snail that in the motion picture *Chico* went to fill the roadrunner's stomach. This white or brown shell is elevated, not depressed (one of the few of this shape in the United States), and grows in such profusion on desert vegetation that it looks like fruit on a richly blooming tree. In Texas also can be found *Helicina*, a small pill-like shell that, unlike all the other land shells in our country, is provided with a shelly door or operculum which closes the aperture when the snail retires. Such operculate snails appear in large numbers of families and species in the West Indies, but the entire North American continent

north of Mexico has exactly three species. Here is a nice puzzle for zoogeographers.

Traveling west from the Mississippi, the land snail fauna becomes steadily more impoverished in the region of the Great Plains. But they never disappear entirely and some minute species occur there in satisfactory numbers. As one approaches the Rocky Mountains, an entirely new group of snails appears. These are called *Oreohelix* and belong to the worldwide family Camaenidae. *Oreohelix* are medium-sized to small snails, and their failure to develop a lip when mature makes them look like the eastern *Anguispira*.

For a time both forms were thought to belong to the same genus. However, Henry A. Pilsbry of the Academy of Natural Sciences in Philadelphia demonstrated their true classification by studying their internal anatomy. He also invented their sonorous name which means *mountain helix, Helix* meaning *a coil*, the old Linnaean name for most of the land snails of the world. These snails live most in large but isolated colonies in favorable spots in the mountains of Colorado, Utah, Idaho, and other western states. The colonies are usually so restricted that unless one actually comes across them, no snails at all can be collected.

In the deserts and on the mountains of New Mexico lives the genus *Sonorella*, named for the Mexican state Sonora. These snails hide deep in the loose rocks of talus slopes and are very difficult to collect. Some species are known from a few dead, weathered specimens. One of the exceptions is *Sonorella odorata* which lives in large numbers in the aspen groves of the Catalina Mountains of Arizona. Its peculiar name was given to it because of its characteristic strong and unpleasant odor, said to resemble that of crushed goldenrod.

In the Huachuca and Chiricahua mountains, especially in the high, forested regions, live the smaller shells of the genus *Ashmunella*, named for the Reverend E. H. Ashmun, a diligent collector of western shells. These look like small *Mesodons* and for a time were included with them in the single genus *Polygyra.* Once again Pilsbry's anatomical studies revealed their true taxonomic postion.

The Sierra Nevada and the Coastal Range mountains form a complete barrier to land snails. West of these ranges the snail fauna makes a startling change. Most of the larger snails we learned to know in the East are gone. Instead we find the genera *Monadenia, Micrarionta,* and *Helminthoglypta,* all members of the endemic American snail family Helminthoglyptidae. The last two genera include snails of moderate size, usually light brown or buff in color, and of a somewhat shining texture. Frequently they are also decorated with a single brown band. They live in the desert regions, and except after rains, are not easy to find.

In the Indio Valley in California lives *Micrarionta indioensis,* a snail that clings to the base of cactus and maguey plants. Hence the would-be collector, armed with a short rake handle, must be ready to contend with these prickly, spiny growths. But one can just as likely turn up a rattlesnake as a retiring snail. For some people this adds a zest to snail collecting which many of us would rather forego. However, some species of these snails can be collected with less danger and trouble, for example *Helminthoglypta californensis,* which lives on Cypress Point near Monterey, California.

*Monadenia* lives in the rainy forest of northern California, Washington, and Oregon. It is a large snail, half again as large as *Mesodon.* The color consists of various shades of buff, yellow, or brown, the base being usually dark brown. Frequently the shell shines like polished mahogany. *Monadenia fidelis beryllica* from Oregon has a beautiful grass- or olive-green base, which is the reason for its subspecific name.

In addition to these native American snails, many also have come here accidentally or were introduced intentionally from the Old World. In several areas of the South about New Orleans, Louisiana, San Antonio, Texas, and Pass-a-Grille, Florida, lives the vineyard snail, *Otala lactea,* which is widely eaten in the Old World by gourmets in Italy and France. It has a heavy, smooth shell, about one inch in diameter, white with brown markings, and a bright chocolate-colored aperture. It is frequently sold in the Italian fish stores in New York City.

In the cemetery of Charleston, South Carolina (and nowhere else!), lives a small white snail that looks like an inverted top. It is called *Helicella elegans,* and probably came over from southern Europe on the roots of some tropical plants. In Maine, in Nova Scotia, and in Quebec, Canada, lives a little hairy snail called *Hygromia hispida,* which probably came to North America from England in the same manner.

There are other introduced snails, but the worst is *Helix apersa* which has become a serious garden pest in southern California. Its shell, not unattractive, is higher than *Mesodon* and has a slightly gleaming surface of a mottled yellow and brown. It lives not on decaying forest plants and mycelium, but on young garden seedlings. Its depredations are frequently very distressing. Another garden pest is the large gray slug, *Limax maximus,* that lives in many city gardens and lots, in the North as well as in the South. It is about four inches long, dirty white in color with large, elongated black areas. The slugs are snails that in the course of evolution have lost their shells or else the shell has degenerated into a small, internal calcareous plate. There are many native slugs that, for the most part, are not harmful, but some of the immigrants have become pests, especially to hothouse owners. Some slugs are almost omnivorous.

One of the prettiest of the introduced snails is the common English garden snail, *Cepea nemoralis,* which has become a fixed resident in many areas

*The garden snail does much damage to plants as it scours them with its rasplike tongue for food*

especially along the Atlantic Coast. It is a handsome snail, about the size of a small *Mesodon*. Its shell has a yellow or orange base color, which may be either bandless or possibly decorated with from one to five brown bands, with a brown lip. These bands have been the subject of intensive studies in heredity as have the color of primroses or the shapes of the fruit fly, *Drosophila*.

W. G. Binney, a well-known American conchologist of the 19th Century, imported several hundred live English garden snails from England in 1857 and freed them in his garden at 222 East Union Street in Burlington, New Jersey. There, according to Binney, "they have thriven well and increased with great rapidity, so that in 1878 the whole town was full of them."

A recent visit made to Burlington showed that this was still so; snails were still living there in empty lots, parks, gardens, and cemeteries, even in the very center of town, Since then *Cepea* colonies have been discovered in such widely separated places as Lexing-

ton, Kentucky; Marion, Massachusetts; and Buffalo and Flushing, New York. It is not known whether these colonies descended from the original Binney importation.

From all appearances the English garden snail has brought a colorful note into the drab appearance of our native eastern snail fauna. They have not proved to be harmful in their new home. Different is the case of a gentleman who in 1948 wrote proudly that he soon hoped to have the eggs of the giant African snail, *Achatina fulica*, hatch in Florida and that the snails "might be developed as an addition to our sources of animal food." Since *Achatina* is a notorious plant predator that has laid waste huge areas in the tropics, this gentleman was severely taken to task by G. D. Hanna of the California Academy of Sciences. At all events, the entire question of deliberate importation of live land snails has now become academic since Congress passed a law forbidding such importations without the express permission of the United States Department of Agriculture.

The subject of land snails is a very large one and has been given very scant treatment here. For the interested amateur naturalist, the study of snails is a field in which the most important discoveries (despite the monumental labors of Gould, Binney, and especially Pilsbry) have yet to be made. Any intelligent observer can add vital facts to the science. And the subjects are easy to study, for land snails are all around us.   —M.K.J.

*Recommended Reading*

**Field Book of Seashore Life**—Roy Waldo Miner. G. P. Putnam's Sons, New York.

## SNAKE

People who suddenly see a snake often react in one of two ways—either they run away screaming, or reach for a stick or a stone with which to kill the reptile.

Either reaction would be foolish, and one would merely demonstrate his ignorance of snakes by so acting. Snakes, far from being dangerous monsters, are really among man's best friends. They destroy countless rats, mice, insects, and other pests, and even the venomous ones are usually glad enough to keep out of harm's way—to slip quickly out of sight or to bite only in self defense. Once one knows something about them, he will find snakes among the most interesting of all wildlife.

Serpents, like lizards, turtles, and crocodiles, are reptiles. Their bodies are clothed with a scaly skin that is dry and feels much like soft leather. Those who claim that snakes are slimy do not know what they are talking about. Usually reptiles are cold to the touch, because their body temperatures may approximate those of their surroundings. They do not maintain a constant temperature as we do (98.6°). During the warmer months snakes are most active, although they avoid lengthy exposure to sun and heat in hot weather. In midsummer most kinds become nocturnal and do their prowling at night. But in the winter, when the ice, snow, or bitter winds would quickly chill them to the freezing point, they seek snug retreats, hibernating until spring beneath big logs, in rock crevices, or other suitable spots. Some, like rattlers, copperheads, and black snakes, congregate in dens or denning areas to which they may return year after year (*See under Reptile*).

### Feeding Habits

Probably there is nothing more amazing about a snake than the way it eats. The average serpent actually can engulf food greater than the diameter of its own head. This is accomplished by a

The eastern diamondback rattlesnake, and its western relative, is the most dangerous poisonous snake in North America

The red-bellied water snake sheds its skin several times each year, the frequency depending on such factors as moisture and temperature

curious arrangement of the teeth-bearing bones. The lower jaw of a snake is divided into two separate parts that are joined at the chin only by elastic tissue that may be stretched for some little distance. Each lower jaw is attached to the corresponding upper jaw in such a way as to permit much freedom of movement, including the ability of the bony structure to get around a large object as it is swallowed. The snake's teeth are shaped like curved needles, all pointing inward. By moving its jaws alternately, food is gradually worked down its gullet. All prey must be swallowed whole, for there is no way for the serpent to tear or bite it into pieces.

Different kinds of snakes employ different methods of overpowering their victims. Some, such as garter snakes, simply seize a frog or fish and swallow it as it struggles to escape. Many others, like the corn and king snakes (and the giant boas and pythons of the tropics), throw a coil or two of their bodies around a bird or rodent and squeeze tightly, literally strangling the victim. Still others, including racers and whip snakes, loop a coil over the prey and press it firmly to the ground. Snakes, in general, are surprisingly efficient in subduing their prey, but it is among the poisonous ones that perfection in this is most nearly achieved. The sharp, hollow fangs inject into the prey animal a deadly venom that, in many cases, kills in a matter of seconds. Swallowing poisoned prey hurts the snake not at all. In fact, the venoms of some kinds of poisonous snakes contain an enzyme that aids digestion.

When food is abundant snakes are apt to gorge themselves and then lie quietly in hiding for several days while digestion proceeds and their appetite returns. The stomach and intestinal juices of snakes are quite powerful and even bones of their prey are dissolved. As far as we know, all snakes are carnivorous; none voluntarily eat vegetable matter. Each species has its own preferences. Some, for example, dote on frogs and toads and will not touch birds; others confine their menus almost exclusively to rodents or to other snakes. From the standpoint of human economics, the rat- and mouse-eaters are the most important and the most worthy of protection. Fortunately, North America is especially rich in serpents of this type.

## Reproduction

Slightly more than half of our kinds of snakes lay eggs. These they deposit in clusters in the midst of rotting logs or stumps, in piles of eaves or manure, or any other spot where the two indispensable requisites are present—moisture

The coral snake, a venomous species, is banded with red and yellow. It is often confused with the harmless king snake that has black bands separating the red and yellow colors

The harmless hog-nosed snake, a resident of dry prairies, has an upturned snout and masses of black pigment on its undersurface. Loud hissing is a sure means of identification

*Snake eggs are usually oblong and the egg shells leathery*

and warmth (the latter furnished in part by the process of decay). The incubation period is not fixed, as it is among birds, for the vagaries of the weather and the variation in the heat and dampness of the material wherein the eggs were laid affect the hatching time. Some serpent eggs have been known to hatch four days after they were laid; others may take three or four months. Each species is consistent, however. Some kinds hatch quickly while others take longer. The number of eggs to a clutch also varies according to the species. A female worm snake may lay only two to five eggs, whereas a female mud snake may lay over a hundred. Only a few kinds remain with their eggs; most serpent mothers abandon them soon after they are laid.

Snake eggs are plain white, cream, or pale yellow. Since they are hidden from the sight of potential enemies they don't need to be streaked, spotted, or otherwise camouflaged as are the eggs of many kinds of birds. The shells are parchmentlike or rubbery. Relatively brief exposure to the open air or sunshine will dry snake eggs sufficiently to kill the embryos within.

Slightly less than half of our snakes bear living young. Instead of spending some time within a shell, the young of these kinds at birth are encased in a thin membrane through which they break soon after they leave the mother's body—sometimes even before. Just as among those species of snakes that lay eggs, there is much variation in the number of the young of those snakes that bear them alive. Rattlers, copperheads, cottonmouths, water, garter, and brown snakes have this type of reproduction. The egg-layers include racers and king, milk, bull, rat, and ringneck snakes.

No matter how a little snake makes its debut into the world, it is on its own from the very start. In the case of the live-bearers the young may remain with the parent for a few hours if the litter and adult are undisturbed, but no attempt is made to stay together and the family soon scatters. It is quite possible for an infant snake never to see its mother again and probably it wouldn't even recognize her as such.

The story that tells of parent snakes protecting their offspring by swallowing them in times of danger crops up continually, but no one has yet produced irrefutable proof that such is the case. Reptilian throats contain no pouches and if the infants slipped down to the stomach they would soon be digested. Such tales seem based upon the killing of a snake that was about to bear a family and inside of which living young ones were found.

## Shedding

Little snakes grow rapidly and it is known that some kinds mature in about three years. Many eat nothing before beginning their first winter of hibernation, but when they emerge into the warmth of spring their appetites are sharp. Periodically they shed their skins, a process that occurs at intervals throughout their lives. For a brief period (a week or more) before the molt takes place, the coloration and pattern become dull and the eyes turn cloudy blue or gray. Vision is imperfect at the time and the snake rests quietly in some hidden retreat. A day or two prior to the actual shedding, the eyes and pattern look almost normal; the skin is then loose and ready to be cast. The snake rubs its nose upon the ground or some rough object and the old epidermis peels backward, under the chin and over the head. And as the snake crawls forward the skin comes off, turning inside out as it does. Usually it is shed in one piece. The new reptilian coat is bright and lovely and the colors are at their best.

## Locomotion

It is difficult to understand how a legless, armless animal can crawl. Yet an inspection of serpentine anatomy and a little study are all that are needed to obtain a good impression of how it is done. Almost all snakes have broad plates extending across their bellies, and each of these overlaps its neighbor to the rear. Each plate is capable of some movement, and a complex arrangement of the muscles within the body makes it possible for the snake to progress forward in almost a straight line by the use of a "caterpillar" action. Each of the backward-pointing scales catches and holds upon slight irregularities of the surface as the animal travels.

There is another and more frequently used type of locomotion that one can observe readily if a snake is placed upon loose sand. The track left by the reptile consists of a series of sidewise loops, first to one side and then to the other. And if one looks closely he will see that at the back, outside portion of each loop, there is a tiny pile of sand. Each pile indicates the spot at which the body obtained a purchase. Without such pivots or without objects such as grass stems, leaves, or stones against which to push, the snake would have a difficult time making progress. Most serpents employ a combination of both methods. In the midst of vegetation snakes seem to flow along at amazing speed, but tests made in recent years show that they move much more slowly than is generally supposed.

## Use of the Tongue

An alert snake runs out its forked tongue with a flickering motion and then quickly withdraws it. The action may be repeated several times, especially if the reptile is on the prowl. Actually it is "tasting" the air, picking up minute particles that the tongue tips carry inside the mouth to two tiny cavities that are lined with sensory cells. Visitors to reptils houses in zoos, noting this habit, exclaim excitedly, "Look at the stinger!" Actually the tongue is soft and harmless. It has nothing to do with a snake's fangs or venom.

## SOME COMMON SNAKES OF THE NORTHEASTERN UNITED STATES

*These 18 species of snakes are among those mostly likely to be encountered in the northeastern United States. Of the three venomous species, only the eastern timber rattlesnake is a serious danger, causing a very high percentage of snake-bite deaths. All snakes, whether venomous or not, are beneficial animals; and although they may occasionally prey on the eggs and young of birds, large snakes are a major factor in the control of rodents that are responsible for many more raids on bird nests. Smaller snakes eat great numbers of insects.*

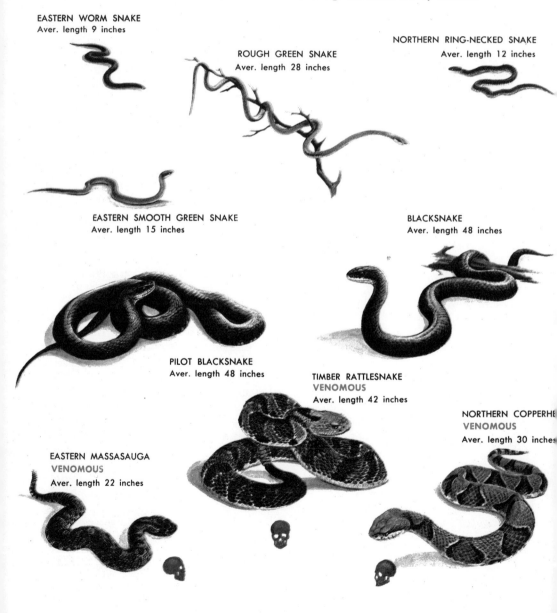

EASTERN WORM SNAKE
Aver. length 9 inches

ROUGH GREEN SNAKE
Aver. length 28 inches

NORTHERN RING-NECKED SNAKE
Aver. length 12 inches

EASTERN SMOOTH GREEN SNAKE
Aver. length 15 inches

BLACKSNAKE
Aver. length 48 inches

PILOT BLACKSNAKE
Aver. length 48 inches

TIMBER RATTLESNAKE
VENOMOUS
Aver. length 42 inches

NORTHERN COPPERHE
VENOMOUS
Aver. length 30 inches

EASTERN MASSASAUGA
VENOMOUS
Aver. length 22 inches

EASTERN RIBBON SNAKE
Aver. length 24 inches

COMMON GARTER SNAKE
Aver. length 24 inches

BUTLER'S GARTER SNAKE
Aver. length 18 inches

DE KAY'S SNAKE
Aver. length 10 inches

RED-BELLIED SNAKE
Aver. length 10 inches

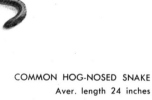

COMMON HOG-NOSED SNAKE
Aver. length 24 inches

EASTERN FOX SNAKE
Aver. length 40 inches

COMMON WATER SNAKE
Aver. length 30 inches

COMMON MILK SNAKE
Aver. length 30 inches

The sense of sight in snakes is well developed and so is the sense of smell. The detection of food and mates by snakes depends largely upon these two faculties. On the other hand, snakes are apparently deaf to airborne sounds; there are no external ear openings. Eyelids also are lacking, and the eyes remain open all the time, even when the serpent is sleeping. The transparent disk that covers each eye is shed along with the rest of the skin.

*Poisonous Snakes*

Venomous snakes are responsible for giving all snakes a bad name. By far the majority of snakes are harmless; only the great constrictors (pythons and anacondas) and a relatively few poisonous species can cause the loss of human life. It has been estimated that less than eight percent of all the kinds of snakes in the world are dangerous to man, and, fortunately, a majority of those are confined to the tropics. Within the borders of the United States one need worry only about rattlesnakes, copperheads, cottonmouths, and coral snakes. In some regions these deadly species are abundant, and, locally, they may outnumber the harmless kinds. In general, however, they are seldom in evidence and present no great human hazard. For every person who dies from snake bite there are 200 who perish as the result of home accidents and another 200 who succumb from automobile accidents. If proper precautions are exercised, such as wearing high leather boots in country that is infested with dangerous snakes, and watching where you put your hands and feet when you go hiking or picnicking, the element of risk is reduced to almost nothing. And modern first aid, if applied at once, can reduce the death rate to less than two percent.

All venomous snakes are equipped with fangs that are merely highly modified teeth, very sharp and hollow. At its base, each fang (normally there are two—one on each side of the head) connects with a poison gland in which the venom is secreted and stored. At the moment of biting, when the fangs are driven deeply into the body of the victim, muscles press against the glands, forcing venom through the fangs. The action is similar to that which takes place in a hypodermic syringe and needle when the doctor presses the plunger.

The poison itself is a liquid, usually clear or slightly cloudy and yellowish in color. It is highly toxic. Venoms vary from species to species. Those of some kinds of snakes attack the bloodstream, destroying corpuscles and preventing clotting. Other kinds attack the nervous system, especially the portion that controls respiration, and death results from an inability to breathe. The speed with which symptoms develop depends upon whether both fangs penetrate the flesh or only one, whether much venom is injected (the snake has some control over the amount), the physical condition of the victim, and also its size. There is a definite ratio between body weight and the amount of poison necessary to kill. Given equal amounts, a mouse dies more quickly than a rabbit, and a child will suffer more than an adult human being.

Snake bite is something to be avoided by all means. A large proportion of accidents occur as the result of careless handling of captive snakes by amateurs. Any person who is bitten should have immediate hospital treatment, and even though no fatality may occur, excruciating pains must be endured and there is a chance of losing a finger or toe, if the bite occurs on either type of digit. It is safest to let poisonous snakes strictly alone.

The accepted first aid procedure includes the application of a tourniquet to impede circulation, cutting through the fang marks with a sharp, sterile instrument, and the injection of antivenomous serum. The last named should be done by a doctor.

Of all the dangerous clan the rattlers

are the most colorful; there are more than a score of species in the United States. Numerous legends have grown up about them, many of them erroneous. They do not have to coil or rattle before biting, nor is it true that the number of segments (or joints) in the rattle corresponds exactly with the number of years the snake has lived. A new segment is added each time the skin is shed, and that normally is several times a year. The rattle is quite brittle, and the terminal portions wear out or break off. It is unusual to find a large specimen with a complete string of rattles. In younger ones the segments are small near the tip and larger toward the tail; the variation coincides with the increase of the snake in size as it grows older. The segments fit together loosely, and when the snake vibrates its tail they rub together, producing the buzzing characteristic of the rattlesnake.

The jointed rattle identifies the rattler, but there are no hard-and-fast rules for telling whether other snakes are dangerous or not. The theory that all venomous serpents have wide, swollen heads will not stand up under close scrutiny. Just look at a picture of the coral snake, one of the dangerous species, and you will see that its head is anything but wide and swollen. If you would like to know the copperhead and cottonmouth when you see them, study colored pictures, or better still visit a zoo or a museum where living ones are on display. Unfortunately there are harmless snakes that look much like these two dangerous kinds, and even the coral snake has its mimics. Several other species of snakes are also ringed with red, yellow, and black, but only the coral snake has the two warning colors—red and yellow (think of a traffic light)—touching each other. In the harmless counterparts black separates the other two colors.

*Snakes Are Useful*

Numerous calculations have been made that prove conclusively that snakes, in general, are useful animals and that they make a marked contribution to our national economy by the prodigious quantities of destructive rodents they consume every year. Like the rodent-eating hawks and owls they occasionally eat birds—even chicks—but the little damage they do is far outweighed by the immense good they accomplish. Farmers have learned that snakes are good animals to encourage.

Since the serpents hold an important place in the balance of nature it is well to let them alone. Let all kinds go their way in peace. Do not kill a snake just

*The patch-nosed snake lays its eggs and then abandons them. In some other snakes eggs are retained in the female and the young are born live*

*The red racer attains lengths of up to five feet. The harmless species feeds largely on lizards and small rodents and moves with startling speed*

*Like a deadly cobra, the harmless hog-nosed snake (above) flattens its head and hisses loudly at suspected enemies. If this fails, it flops over on its back and remains motionless, feigning death (below)*

because it is a snake. If it is dangerous, one should avoid it so he will not be bitten. If it is harmless the chances are it is of real value.                    —Ro.C.

*Recommended Reading*

**Amphibians and Reptiles of Western North America**—Robert C. Stebbins. McGraw-Hill Book Company, Inc., New York.
**Field Guide to Reptiles and Amphibians**—Roger Conant. Houghton Mifflin Company, Boston.
**Handbook of Snakes**—Albert H. Wright and Anna A. Wright. Comstock Publishing Associates, Cornell University Press, Ithaca, New York.
**The Natural History of North American Amphibians and Reptiles**—James A. Oliver. Van Nostrand, Princeton, New Jersey.
**Rattlesnakes: Their Habits, Life Histories and Influence on Mankind**—Laurence M. Klauber. University of California Press, Berkeley, California.
**Reptiles and Amphibians of the Northeastern States**—Roger Conant. Zoological Society of Philadelphia, Philadelphia.
**The Reptile World**—Clifford H. Pope. Alfred A. Knopf, Inc., New York.
**Snakes Alive and How They Live**—Clifford H. Pope. Viking Press, New York.

### Care of Snakes in Captivity

Generally, children are not afraid of snakes. Some of them may be because they have seen their parents or other adults frightened at the sight of snakes in the garden. Children usually like snakes, and can easily be induced to make pets of them. This is a good interest for youngsters, provided the snakes are properly housed and adequately cared for.

Snakes kept in captivity have considerable value in teaching youngsters the role of these animals in the environment, their value as eaters of insects, and as controllers of other animals. Some snakes eat mice, some eat rats and gophers, but whatever their diet, snakes have a definite place among those creatures that tend to regulate and keep in balance the animal populations of a given environment. Obviously, if youngsters are going to keep snakes as pets, they must look after them properly, keep their cages clean, feed them regularly and adequately, and see to it that they have a constant supply of clean water.

A good snake cage requires that the animal have an adequate amount of air; it should also be roomy enough so that the snake can move around, stretch its long body, and get the kinks out of its tremendously long backbone. A rule of thumb would be that the cage be as long as two-thirds the length of the snake. There is one kind of cage that is the result of many trials with designs that would satisfy the requirements of proper housing, while exhibiting the snake in such a way that it could be readily observed. The basic structure is built of wood—it would be scrap lumber if a child wanted to build his own. The sides are made of pieces slightly over an inch thick, so that they will not warp. They are cut so that they slope to the rear at about a 60° angle. Some expert help may be needed to saw the groove on the insides of the end pieces, where the glass cover will slide. A wood-working hobbyist with a power saw can easily make such a groove, which has to be wide enough for double-thick window glass. The cage has a wooden floor, a strip of wood across the front, another across the back extending about halfway up. The door forms the upper part of the back. This is hinged so that it falls to the rear. This allows the cage to be easily cleaned, the animal easily fed and watered, and simplifies removing the snake for the petting and handling necessary to make it tame. The door is a simple thing, made with strips of wood and screen wire. A piece of bronze or copper wire screen is sandwiched between the two strips of wood on all four sides, so that no rough edges are present. The door ventilates the cage, allowing plenty of air circulation. It is placed high in the cage so that the normal meanderings of the snake do not bring its nose in contact with the wire. The door is latched at both ends. A hasp can fasten one side to support, if necessary, a padlock.

This cage is designed for harmless

snakes, not for poisonous ones. The glass used is double-thick window glass, obtainable at any hardware store. To house poisonous snakes, it would be necessary to use safety glass, or glass that has been reenforced with wire.

To finish the job, paint the cage. On the outside, this can be any color; for the inside, use aluminum paint. This will reflect sufficient light to make the colors of the snake show up well, without having the glare and easy-soiling qualities of white paint. The result is a good-looking exhibit cage, which is also safe and sanitary for the pet snake.

An old, rough, picturesque piece of wood in the cage is for a purpose, as well as for appearance. The purpose is to make available a rough surface on which the snake can rub itself when it comes time to molt its skin. Reptiles need larger skins as they become bigger. To accomplish the change from the old to the new, they literally turn their skins inside out. This can often be watched when snakes are kept as pets and is always fascinating to see. The new skin is formed beneath the old, and when the change is complete, there is the pet with a new, brightly colored skin, and more handsome than ever.

There should be some litter in the bottom of the snake cage. First a little clean sand, and then a few pine needles or some old leaves from the forest floor. The sand will help when it comes time to clean the cage, and the leaf litter will provide a light cover, under which the pet can partially hide.

It should be remembered that constant feeding with resultant constant growth is natural in the snake world during the warm season of the year. Snakes also have to store within their bodies food to carry them through the winter hibernation. Thus you have the job of providing the snake with a steady supply of such foods as frogs and worms. If these natural foods are not available, you can often get a snake to feed on strips of raw fish or on raw, lean hamburger. This is best rolled around the end of a piece of string, or fed to the snake from the end of a thin stick. Fresh water in a low bowl should be in the cage at all times.

Another important thing to remember is that a snake cannot live if kept in full sunlight for long periods of time. Snakes have no way of controlling the temperature of their blood stream the way mammals do. Their body temperature is always near that of the air temperature. That is why they are more active when it is warm and sluggish when it is cold. As a general rule, snake cages should be kept in a shady place, or where the sun shines only for a brief period during the day.

A good practice for most people would be to keep a snake for a pet only for a short period of time. Then, when a new one is found release the one that has been captive for a while, and keep the new one. Also, inasmuch as snakes are easily found, the thing for most people to do is to release their pet snakes in the late summer or early fall, and just put the snake cage away until the following spring. This is usually much better than trying to keep a snake in captivity over winter.

Which snake makes the best pet? There is no hard and fast rule, but the thing to remember is that is must be one of the harmless ones. Usually it is one that is common. The garter snake fills the bill for practically the entire United States; also, the garter snake feeds well in captivity on either worms or frogs. Ribbon snakes are satisfactory also, as are the small red-bellied, ringneck, and DeKay's, or brown, snake. The black snake and milk snakes are handsome, nonpoisonous ones, but the blacks are apt to be of large size, and the milk snakes, the great mousers, usually will not eat in captivity.

Now a word of caution about the snakes to stay clear of. Rattlesnakes, wherever they are found, are obviously not animals to make pets of. In the South are the dangerous water moccasins, or cotton-mouths, and the beautifully colored coral or harlequin snakes. While usually noc-

*Snakes are fascinating and beneficial animals that are often needlessly persecuted*

*Many snakes do well in captivity if kept in a well-ventilated cage floored with sand*

turnal, the copperhead is another snake to treat with respect. The snakes just mentioned are all poisonous and capable of injecting a dangerous dose of toxin by biting with their needlelike fangs.

The common water snakes, with a range which covers the entire eastern half of the country, are relatives of the garter snakes. As their name implies, they are found near bodies of water. While not poisonous, they are more vicious than most snakes, and can inflict wounds that sometimes become infected. Besides being wild in nature, they usually defecate when disturbed, and so add a bad odor to their other bad attributes. In general, then, it could be said that the small, common, harmless snakes found around the garden are the ones most likely to make the best pets.           —E.A.M.

*Recommended Reading*

**The Book of Wild Pets**—Clifford Moore. Charles T. Branford Company, Newton Centre, Massachusetts.

## SNIPE
### Common Snipe
**Other Common Names**—American snipe, Wilson's snipe, jacksnipe, bog snipe, marsh snipe, alewife-bird, shad spirit

**Scientific Name**—*Capella gallinago*
**Family**—Scolopacidae (woodcock, snipe, and sandpipers)
**Order**—Charadriiformes
**Size**—Length, 10 to 11½ inches
**Range**—Nests from Alaska south and eastward across Canada to Labrador, south to Pennsylvania and New Jersey, west to California, Arizona, Colorado, Nebraska, Iowa, northern Illinois, Ohio, and Michigan

### Habits of the Common Snipe

When bottomlands brighten beneath April showers, along brooks in which the alewives throng up from the sea, the common, or Wilson's, snipe blow in on the south wind and pitch into their green meadow world. Occasionally one may glimpse them flickering through the gloom, or dropping among the cattails in sweet water marshes. Sometimes one may see one far up in the ruddy evening sky, zigzagging across the darkening water. Even when bound for some definite objective, this marshbird finds it impossible to travel in a straight line.

Snipe will find a marshy pocket on a farm even it it is not half an acre in extent. Such a miniature marsh oozes from the top of a hill near Califon,

New Jersey, in the center of a rocky pasture much frequented by killdeer plovers. A single snipe will often alight there during migrations, almost as if it had scented the place while drifting past among the evening clouds.

When a common snipe drops in at Califon, a hundred may revisit some larger fen at no great distance, for they often arrive in a cloud. As the woodcock is the genius of open woods and upland alder runs, so the snipe is the familiar spirit of grassy rivers, freshwater morasses, and brackish meadows. It haunts more acres of such terrain than any other bird, ranging throughout North America, Central America, and South America to southern Brazil.

Old-time sportsmen accustomed to hearing its sharply uttered *Scape! Scape!* as it flushes before their dogs, seldom thought of this bird as a minstrel of the night.

Such, in a humble way, it certainly is. Its winnowing notes, strangely elusive and ephemeral, have a spiritlike remoteness when they float down from the gloaming above some verdant river bottom. Sometimes one glimpses the bird through the dusk in the spring. It circles at such heights that one frequently hears only the ventriloquial sounds, now here, now there. The observer must take the bird itself for granted.

These sounds are not vocal. The snipe rises at a steep angle and describes an immense aerial ellipse. Then, slanting downward and side-slipping, the outer quills of its wings and tail produce the melody. Similarly the "bleat" of the European snipe is thought to be made by its tail feathers.

Whatever the instrument producing the sounds, they seem to be attuned to the ears of some female, lurking in the grassy wilderness below. They recall the less musical but more familiar lay of the American woodcock. These two upland shorebirds have many points in common: long, sensitive bills for probing for worms in the fens, mottled plumage on back and shoulders matching typical surroundings, and a decided liking for the dusk. Both species migrate by night.

The mystery of the migration of the snipe—here today but gone tomorrow—also reminds us of woodcock ways. Both species revisit the same favored spots year after year, and no other species of game was more shamefully overgunned in the days of its greatest abundance. To cite a familiar example, James J. Pringle, gunning snipe near Bayou Teche, southwestern Louisiana, killed 69,087 in 20 years. In November 1874, he killed 1,445 snipe in six shooting days.

No other sportsman equaled Pringle's score, but many tried to do so, and when the birds were at length removed from the list of legal game, they were in danger of extermination. Of late years the common snipe has been gaining slightly in numbers and so it has been made legal game again—a measure deplored by all good sportsmen.

Snipe are among the few shorebirds whose nests may be seen by observers in our middle latitudes. The nest is a wisp of grass whirled into a circle in a marshy meadow, sometimes on a patch of floating island, or knitted into a sedgy tuft at a slight elevation beside some creek or run. April 29 to May 26 is the nesting period in New England and the Middle Atlantic States.

It builds its nest early, and spring peepers seem to hail its construction with shrill applause. But before the chicks pip the shell the peepers' cries will have yielded to the *Trrrrrrump! Trrrrrrump!* of bullfrogs. While it is building, the male snipe struts before his mate, his head thrown back like a miniature turkey cock, his wings trailing, and his tail spread. Now and then the snipe spirals up a little way to display his charms in flight. But he soon pitches down again, with twittering notes to his mate.

He is far from silent on the ground. Sometimes a marsh will become noisy with unseen rails, all cackling at once.

*Wilson's snipe lives in woodland meadows, river bottoms, and freshwater marshes*

*A newly hatched Wilson's snipe has an exaggerated bill characteristic of its species*

A big flight of common snipe sound off in the same manner, but in a higher, shriller key. One moment the racket is almost ear-splitting, but the next is as silent as death.

One occasionally sights a snipe nest raised some inches above the floor of the bog. The eggs, very large for the size of the bird, are pear-shaped, whitish or gray, with heavy blotches of brown, umber, or black on the larger ends. Lusterless when placed beside woodcock eggs, they bear patterns not readily noticed in the grass.

The female snipe broods her eggs to the strains of an all-night, marshland orchestra. The solitary bittern sounds the loud bassoon, while the bubblethroats of a thousand tree frogs furnish the music of fifes and piccolos. If the nest is in the deep South in early spring the boom of distant bull alligators sustains the bass.

When at length the snipe chicks pip the shell and trip forth into the fen, they will find limitless insect food on which to fatten. Like the young of all other Limicolae (snipes and sandpipers) they are precocious and quickly learn to feed themselves. One will never see a mother snipe shoving worms down their throats as parent robins must do for their young. Like woodcock, snipe probe for worms, but also consume mosquitoes and their larvae, mayflies, damselflies, cutworms, grasshoppers, wireworms water beetles, and click beetles. They also eat the seeds of various weeds and water plants in the meadows. They can swim, dive, or wade equally well, and have been known to alight in brush and low trees. No other member of their order is more versatile.

Although the common snipe and woodcock wear somewhat similar protective patterns on their backs, their underparts are markedly different. The grayer, speckled plumage of the smaller common snipe, and its whitish belly contrast sharply with the russet breast of the woodcock. In feeding, the snipe jabs its long bill

*Common snipe*

vertically and repeatedly, whereas the woodcock holds its mandibles deep in the mud.

Snipe have always been more numerous in the northeastern United States in the spring than in the fall. The reason is that on the southward trek large numbers fly out to sea and escape notice unless driven inland by severe gales. In such cases they suddenly throng the shores of the Atlantic Coast at Cape Cod, Monomoy, Block Island, Nantucket, Martha's Vineyard, and Montauk Point. They are now, and always have been, eccentric and unpredictable.

Censuses of snipe marshes in Maine, Massachusetts, Rhode Island, New York, Long Island, New Jersey, Georgia, and Florida—all places where snipe were abundant many years ago—have failed to find any such increase of snipe as would justify putting these birds back on the gamebird list. Here and there,

*Wilson's snipe constructs a grass-lined depression in a marshy place in which to lay its three or four speckled, olive eggs*

perhaps, there may be some improvement. In certain marshy pockets northwest of St. Augustine, Florida, snipe have gained slightly, and the same is true of the estuaries of the Wakulla and St. Marks rivers 15 miles south of Tallahassee. But 89,000 acres of that region are included in the St. Marks Federal Wildlife Sanctuary where birds are rigidly protected. Any such gunning pressure as the old-timers used to exert might exterminate the species.

One never recalls his semioccasional experiences with the elusive snipe without inhaling again the aroma of autumn marshland, or admiring its brown tapestry outlined by the carmine border of swamp maples, or hearing the odd, staccato cries with which the birds lifted free of the grass and darted erratically away.                  —H.M.H.

**SNOW** (*See under Frost*)

**SNOW PLANT**
**Other Common Names**—None
**Scientific Name**—*Sarcodes sanguinea*
**Family**—Monotropaceae (Indian-pipe family)
**Range**—Cascade Mountains, southern Oregon, south to southern California
**Habitat**—Coniferous forests, arid Transition Zone
**Time of Blooming**—May to June

Snow plants push their way up through beds of pine needles in high mountains. They do not come up through the snow, but grow where snow

*Snow plant*

has recently melted. Sometimes a late snow will cover them and then melt away. All parts of the plant above ground are red. The roots are white and rolled into brittle balls. Very often there are several of these plants growing near each other, from 6 to 15 inches high. The law says they must not be picked or taken up by the roots.

## SOIL
*Plants as Makers of Soil*

A house, it is often said, does not become a home until it has been lived in. Neither does the surface of the earth become soil until it, too, is lived in by long generations of plants and animals. We know that soil is necessary for good plant growth. It may surprise us to learn that good plant growth is necessary for soil.

This may suggest the old riddle of which came first, the hen or the egg, but the answer is easier. There had to be plants before there could be soil. No human being was on hand to watch the beginning of this process, but we can surmise pretty well from what we see today how it must have happened. The first simple plants which moved from water to land were able to survive on raw mineral surface. As they lived there, they altered their surroundings physically and chemically, and when they died their remains were added to the minerals in which they had lived, changing and enriching them. In this way they ultimately—and literally— paved the earth for new kinds of plants whose requirements were more exacting than theirs.

Our great forests, fertile prairies, and rich cultivated fields of today have been made possible by this long process of living and dying.

To begin at the beginning, the rock materials of the earth's surface must be broken into fragments before soil can be formed. When land is lifted from the water, exposing the old sea

or lake bed, this work has already often been done by the waves. Rock fragments in the form of sand, or silt, or still finer, clay, are ready for pioneer plants to begin their work. The same thing happens when sand is blown out of a dry river bed, or when a stream, changing its course, leaves sand and gravel exposed (*See under Rock Formation*).

In such instances, the first invaders are usually annual plants whose seeds are blown or washed over the surface. These are the kind of plants we call weeds. Since they are seldom usable by man directly, we often overlook the immense good they do in healing over the bare surface on which they can live. Weeds are nature's "scar tissue." They hold the raw mineral stuff in place,

*Lichens pioneer on hard rock surfaces and help to begin the cycle by which rock is broken down into smaller particles from which soil is formed*

encourage the invasion of animals whose droppings and remains add organic matter, and start the building of what we know as soil. Equally important, they afford shade and protection for other, more permanent kinds of plants. Like the advance guard of an army, pioneer plants are a sacrifice for those that follow them. Hardly ever can the seedlings of the first invaders thrive under the protection that their own parents create.

But let us go back for a moment to the rock materials. Often there is exposed, not sand, or silt or clay, but hard bare rock. Upon this the forces of the atmosphere begin their slow work of wear and breakage—a process called, properly enough, *weathering*. Freezing and thawing, wetting and drying, slow erosion of water and of wind all play a part in loosening the material of the exposed rock.

But the atmosphere does not work alone in this process of weathering. Like prisoners on a rockpile, whose job is to make little ones out of big ones, there are simple forms of plant life that help in this task of breaking up hard rock. Such plants are the lichens, whose work can be seen on cliffs, rocks, boulders, and even on the tombstones of an old cemetery (*See under Lichen*).

Each lichen is in reality a dual plant composed of threads of fungus which hold entrapped green cells of algae. These algae make food for both. In form, lichens may be like a scabby crust upon the stone, or tufted, or even like an irregular leathery leaf. In color they run the scale of pastel shades from burnt orange to purple, being most often soft gray-green.

Clinging tightly to the rock face, these lichens work upon it in one or both of two ways. They may secrete acids which dissolve the cementing substance of the rock, loosening the granules between. Or they may, with the alternate swelling and shrinking of wet and dry weather, pull upon the rock and loosen particles

from its surface. This action is not unlike the tension of drying glue upon the skin. When hot, the glue spreads out and clings; when cool and dry, it shrinks and pulls.

If one will take the trouble, either in the mountains or the graveyard, to scrape off a bit of lichen with a penknife, he can frequently see (or feel with his teeth) the gritty rock particles on its underside. And one can generally note that the surface from which it has come is freshly pitted.

The rock particles produced by these miniature quarries are washed or blown into crevice or depression with the products of atmospheric weathering. In such pockets of material, as in the cracks of an old sidewalk or abandoned highway, the spores of mosses and the seeds of tiny annuals find lodging and grow. With them come small invertebrates that work and rework the deposit (*See Invertebrate*). In larger crevices woody plants find anchor and their growing roots loosen the rock fragments through which they must make their way. Each growing season adds its contribution of dark organic material, while the work of the atmosphere goes on unceasingly.

Meanwhile the extremes of elevation and depression are slowly being modified—projections wearing down and valleys filling up. In the end, what has been hard rock becomes covered with a mantle of weathered material in which vegetation is at home. Soil has been formed.

The place to see the results of this long process is a fresh cut—say a trench or a roadside—where the natural forest or prairie is still in place. Here we can see soil in its third dimension—that of depth. If one examines soil only on the surface, seeing nothing more than length and breadth, he misses much that has been going on beneath the surface.

A road-cut in the forest will show a thin dark layer on top. This is the rich leaf mold, formed by the accumulation and fermentation of wet leaves of many seasons. In it is a teeming population of insects and other small animals, of fungi and bacteria which help return the fallen leaves to the soil. The leaf-mold layer is a busy chemical laboratory.

Below it are lighter layers, changed both physically and chemically by plant activity. Through them run the roots of trees, absorbing minerals which are carried out into the branches and leaves, from which they ultimately find their way to the surface of the ground when the leaves and branches fall. Into the dark top layer of the soil, then, come minerals from the lower depths, brought up by the roots and reworked by the green leaves (together with water and gases from the air) into organic compounds which form rich humus when

they decay. To this humus wandering animals also contribute their droppings and remains.

Beneath the zone occupied by great tree roots lies the parent rock-stuff, whatever it may be—limestone, granite, shale.

If our road-cut is in the prairies of Iowa or eastern Nebraska, we find a different picture. There the plants are the grasses and legumes of the prairie, whose fine, tangled roots form a dense turf. These roots fill the mineral soil to depths of three to five feet or more. With them are mingled the burrows of many animals, small and large. Generation after generation, roots and animals live and die, forming the rich black humus which is the bread basket of this

*Unlike the soils of the forest which concentrate organic material and minerals in the shallow black layer of rotting leaves, the black top layer of prairie soil is deep. Below it, are two zones— one influenced by the vegetation above, the other the parent material. Here the plants are grasses and legumes whose fine, tangled roots form a dense turf. These roots fill the mineral soil to depths*

*of three to five feet or more. With them are mingled the burrows of many animals, small and large. Generation after generation, roots and animals live and die, forming rich black humus. The section to the left shows 20 inches of prairie topsoil. The picture (right) is a typical profile of prairie soil in western Washington showing the thick dark topsoil layer—and the lighter subsoil layer below it*

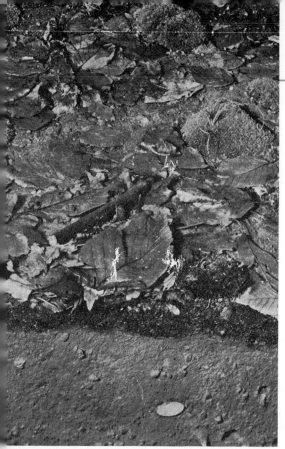

*A cross-section of forest soil reveals a top layer of leaf-mold. In it is a teeming population of insects and other small animals, and of fungi and bacteria which help break down the fallen leaves into soil. The leaf-mold layer is a busy chemical laboratory. Leaves, mosses, bark, roots, and small plants contribute to this layer*

country. (*See Grassland under Grass*).

Unlike the soils of the forest which concentrate organic material and minerals in the shallow black zone of rotting leaves, the black top layer of the prairie is deep. Below it, as in the forest soils we find two zones—one, influenced by the vegetation above, the other and deeper, the parent material.

In every climate of the world where plants can grow, they leave their impress on the soil. Naturally, this effect is least in the desert, where plant life is scarce and wide-spaced, and where dead plant-stuff tends to dry out rather than to rot. Contrary to what one might suppose, desert plants do not root

deeply. Instead, they must depend upon the rare rains that merely wet the surface layers, and it is to these layers that their roots are confined. Instead of being brought to the surface by roots, minerals are concentrated in the top of desert soils by the force of evaporation, which is intense (*See under Desert*).

An opposite extreme is to be found in the frozen arctic tundra, where minerals are locked in perpetual ice a short distance below the surface. There lowly plants grow during the brief summers, and die below as they grow at the top. Thus the passing of time brings the accumulation of undecayed plant remains, peat or muskeg, lying on the rocks below. Such soil is almost purely of plant origin.

In the hot and humid tropics the growth of vegetation is more rapid than anywhere else on earth. But so, too, is the process of decay, while the torrential rains tend to dissolve out surface minerals in great quantities. As a result, the soils of the tropics are tremendously fertile for the first year or two of cultivation, and then become unproductive.

We have discussed mostly the larger plants, with roots, stems, and leaves. No less important in soil formation are those tiny, often invisible plants—the fungi and bacteria. These, as we have said, bring about the decay of plant and animal remains. Such decay returns minerals to the soil. It also produces spongy dark humus, which will hold three times it own weight in water, permitting it to soak slowly into the ground (*See under Fungus.*)

Bacteria also enrich the soil in another way—by bringing nitrogen from the air into the soil and transforming it into materials that plants can use in making protein foods, so necessary to all life. Some of these nitrogen fixers, as they are called, live free in the soil, getting their energy from humus. Others live as guests on the roots of clovers, beans, and other legumes. The abundant nitrogen in prairie soils is due largely to the great numbers of kinds of native legumes that grow with the prairie grasses. There are over 80 kinds of such native legumes in Nebraska alone (*See Legume*).

Wherever man has cultivated the soil, he has interrupted the natural processes by which it was formed. Often, especially when he has grown clean-cultivated crops in rows, the fertile dark top layer has been washed away, making the soil far less productive than it was. Unless the washing has exposed the hard parent material, it is frequently possible to improve, or rebuild, the soil by skillful use of plantlife.

One way to do this is by allowing the depleted land to grow up in forest. The forest may be planted, then protected against grazing and fire. Or if the climate is favorable and the land is abandoned, trees will gradually become established by natural means, slowly forming a dark surface layer as we have seen. This process is effective, but slow, and may require fifty or a hundred years before the trees can be harvested and the land put back into cultivation. Even then, care has to be

*A modern soil conservation measure combines floodwater retaining structures with complete conservation treatment of the area draining into them*

taken so that the new-formed soil is not quickly washed away and the land once more made useless.

Where the land is fairly level and otherwise well suited to agriculture, it can best be restored by the use of grass and legume meadows, whose effect is much like that of the native prairies, already described. The first step is to analyze the depleted soil residue, to determine what minerals have been washed away. Nearly always these include lime and phosphorus, often potash. These must be replaced when the ground is plowed and seeded. Frequently a cover crop of some tall grass such as rye is used to start with. This may be allowed to grow for a time, then be disk-harrowed into the surface to provide organic matter, before the other grasses and the legumes are planted. Or it may be used as a nurse crop to afford them protection while they get started.

When the meadow is well established, it may be grazed lightly, thus adding animal manure to the ground. Or it may be clipped from time to time and the clippings allowed to rot. After a sufficient time, the deepening green color of the meadow will show that the bacteria in the legume roots have added considerable nitrogen to the soil, and the soil itself will show a darker color. It is then ready for use, either as regular pasture for a period of years, or for cultivation. If cultivated, it must be returned to grass and legumes at intervals, generally for at least two years out of every four or five.

In addition, when other crops are grown, the soil must be protected from further washing, as it is under natural conditions. This is accomplished in various ways. Rows of cultivated crops should be planted across the slope, instead of up and down hill. If the slope is fairly steep, alternate strips of row crops and meadow should be used. And so far as possible, no land should be allowed to lie bare during the winter months. Some kind of cover crop, such as rye, ought to be planted between the rows of corn or cotton at the last cultivation, so that when winter rains come the surface will be protected.

The natural forests and prairies not only make the soils that feed us, but they furnish the model that we must follow, so far as we can, if we are to protect, preserve, and improve those soils after we have cleared them and put them to the plow.　　—P.B.S.

*Recommended Reading*

**Factors of Soil Formation**—Hans Jenny. McGraw-Hill, New York.
**Living Earth**—Peter Farb. Harper & Brothers, New York.
**Textbook of Botany**—Transeau, Sampson and Tiffany. Harper & Brothers, New York.
**The Soils that Support Us**—C.E. Kellogg. The Macmillan Company, New York.
**Soil**—The Yearbook of Argiculture, 1957. U.S. Government Printing Office, Washington, 25, D.C.

**Importance of Soil to Wildlife**

Some of the best "birding" spots near towns and suburban villages can be reached by the wood trails that lead off dirt roads. An open glade that ends in a cow pasture is always rewarding. A morning when one crosses the little brook and enters this charming spot he is more conscious than ever of the number and variety of things that live there.

Some people could have taken such a country walk and, being too busy with thoughts about themselves, would see nothing but the grass and the trees but not those who are alert. Their eyes are keen and they see many things. A flicker flies from a large anthill where it has been grubbing with its long bill; a little party of sulphur butterflies hovers around a wet, muddy spot on the path. A male song sparrow sings from a bush top and dashes after another song sparrow that has trespassed on his territory. Chipmunks scamper under the rocks of an old stone wall. Dragonflies hawk the air, and everywhere there are living things, crawling, hopping, or flying.

It may never occur to one how much the soil had to do with the lives of these creatures. Many of them forage among the plants or scratch or grub in the debris at the grass roots. The soil seems to have a great fascination for many kinds of wildlife.

To discover why the soil is important to wildlife, one might take a sample of the soil so that we may see what is in it. A small trowel and a pail used for transporting plants to the garden will be handy. A handful of surface dirt and debris from an open grassy spot reveals an ant, a tiny spider, and several other small creatures. This looks promising, and is dumped into the pail and a section of earth 12 inches long, 6 inches wide, and 4 inches deep is carefully scooped out with the trowel and dumped in with it. One finds by probing deeper into the soil that only an occasional grub or earthworm can be found deeper than three to four inches. Most of the small animal life lives near the surface. One-half square foot of soil is quite enough to analyze, so a piece of cloth may be tied tightly over the pail to prevent anything from crawling out.

*What Was in the Soil—*

After returning to one's home, one should examine the dirt, bit by bit, on a piece of white cardboard.

The pailful of earth may be put on the center of the work table and carefully picked over a handful of it at a time, or a piece of cardboard. If an insect or worm is found, it may be picked up with tweezers and dropped into a little glass medicine vial. With a dozen people working, it does not take long to run through the whole pail. The pail itself and its cloth covering should be carefully examined, too, so that nothing will be missed. Some of the tinier things can be very easily overlooked. Some will be tiny,

pale insects. These are springtails, and they are very hard to catch, too, because they jump when the tweezers touchs them.

When the job is finished, one should try to analyze the contents of the vial. To do this, one should have the help of several good books on insects and other invertebrates. An analysis of the animal contents of a half-square foot of soil may show the following:

| | |
|---|---:|
| Earthworms | 2 |
| Sowbugs | 6 |
| Centipedes | 3 |
| Millipedes | 10 |
| Mites | 6 |
| Spiders | 1 |
| Ants | 15 |
| Fly pupae | 30 |
| Aphids | 4 |
| Beetles | 4 |
| Springtails | 14 |
| Unidentified | 20 |
| Total | 115 |

One hundred and fifteen invertebrates in a half square foot of earth means two hundred and thirty per square foot! What would that be per acre— This is easily determined with a paper and pencil or on a blackboard.

43,560 (sq. ft. per acre)
x230

10,018,800

More than 10 million small animals to the acre is reason enough that the soil is such a favorite feeding ground. Little wonder that robins, song sparrows, moles, and mice spend so much of their time there.

Of course, some soil samples studied are especially productive. Woodland soil would be less productive in itself because many of the small creatures would be scattered throughout the undergrowth and in the leafy canopy of the trees overhead. It would be almost impossible to get an accurate count.

It will be noted that most of the insects are in the ground debris and in the top three to four inches of soil.

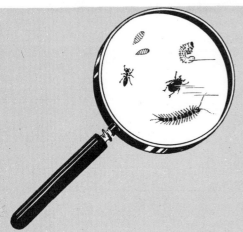

*For every plant and animal on the earth's surface, there are multitudes in the soil. Most of these are in the top three or four inches*

*Millions of insects and other inverte-brates live in one acre of topsoil*

*Without microorganisms it would be impossible for dead plant and animal matter to be utilized by living plants and animals*

*In a single gram of topsoil, millions of microorganisms are at work breaking down dead matter in the process known as decay*

If a small sample of this same rich surface soil were placed beneath a powerful microscope, great numbers of tiny organisms can be seen—tiny plant and animals forms. These are micro-organisms; millions, or even billions, exist in a single gram of soil. These micro-organisms are perhaps as necessary as anything on earth. Without them life would stop. They form the link between the living and the dead. They trans-form dead plants and animals into a condition on which living plants and animals can be nourished.

The microorganisms and insects, birds, mammals, man himself, and his crops—are all dependent on one an-other. They all get their life from the soil and return to the soil when they die.

### Birds and the Soil

If the life-giving topsoil were to go and the land be made lean, it is logical that birds would be less common, too. Some of the highest densities of birds live in swamps and marshes. In one cattail marsh, the density may be 16 birds per acre. This is what one would expect, considering the rich organic content of the mud and water. Most habitats have between three and six birds per acre. An exhausted abandoned field has about two birds per acre, a park in a large city less than one and a half. The lowest density of all is to be found on a fill, where much inorganic mud and gravel has been pumped onto a drained salt marsh. In such places there may be only six birds on 100 acres.

## A Good Bird Population Is A Sign of Healthy Land

Scientific studies have shown that not only are the animals dependent on the soil but that the soil is dependent on animal life.

As animal activities in soils increase, soil structure, fertility, and cover are improved. Vertebrate animals, such as the mammals and the birds, occassionally have as great an effect on the soil as the lower forms of animal life.

The top layer of earth, which is so full of organic life, has been likened to the frosting on a cake. We have lost much of the topsoil of the American continent and are getting down to the less productive subsoil. When the topsoil goes, everything that depends upon it is affected—the small creatures, the birds, and the man and his crops.

## Erosion

Much of this loss of topsoil has been the result of *erosion or a wearing away* by wind and water. To demonstrate water erosion in its simplest form, take a large piece of wallboard and prop it up to present a slight slope. Then take a watering can and sprinkle a quart of water at the top. It slides off almost instantly. Place an old piece of thick carpet on the board and repeat the sprinkling. Very little water runs through, at first, and the dribble continues for some time.

The wallboard is like a hillside with a slope; the can of sprinkled water like rainfall, the bare surface represents plowed fields. The carpet represents natural ground cover, either grass or woodlands.

Over the bare fields, improperly plowed, the water comes down, taking with it the rich topsoil. In the second experiment, the water sinks into the cover and is released slowly. Very little, if any, soil is washed away.

## A Soil-Erosion Exhibit

From this demonstration one can make a soil-erosion exhibit for the nature room or classroom from the following materials:

> Two wooden boxes (three feet long, 1 foot wide, four inches deep)
> Two small pieces of screen-door mesh
> Two large glass jars
> Two sprinkling cans
> Table for the exhibit
> Sod and moss for the first box
> Light sandy soil for second box
> Two pieces of tin
> Two funnels
> Tar paper
> The procedure is as follows:

1. The wooden boxes are made in the workshop. One end of each box is left open.
2. A strip of fine screening is tacked over the open end of each box.
3. The boxes are lined tightly with tar paper—except for the screened ends.
4. The boxes are propped up on the table at a slope (10 to 15 degrees), the screened ends at the bottom.
5. The tin is bent into a trough to catch the water at the lower end of each box, just off the table. A hole is made in the center of the trough, through which the water can run.
6. Beneath each trough is placed a large glass jug and tin funnel.
7. In box No. One, the bottom is covered with sod and moss.
8. In box No. Two, the bottom is covered with the light sandy soil.

When the exhibit has reached this stage it is ready for a tryout. The water is sprinkled slowly so as to have the

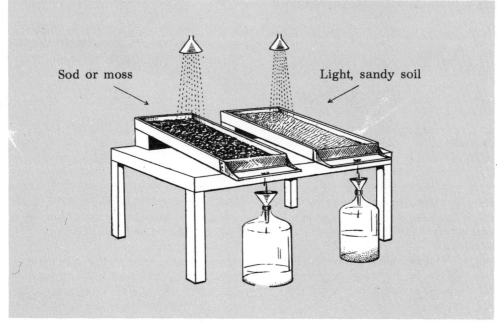

*A soil erosion exhibit shows the effect of water runoff on unprotected soil*

same effect as ordinary rain. It takes about twenty minutes to empty each can. Care must be taken to sprinkle the soil surface evenly.

The result will be very convincing. The light sandy soil, without protective covering, allows a much more rapid runoff of water. When the water in the jars has settled, much more sediment will be found in jar No. Two than in jar No. One.

### Will America Wash Into the Sea?

The Mississippi River has always been silted, but since the coming of the settlers, it is estimated that an additional 300 million tons of rich soil are dumped from the fields of the Mississippi Valley into the Gulf of Mexico each year. The rivers in South Carolina and Georgia are also almost red with mud. They, too, were probably quite clear once upon a time. Statistics say the Southeast has improverished 97 million acres of its surface soil—97 million acres—an area larger than the two Carolinas and Georgia put together. One likes to think

of our country as a rich land, but at this rate how long will it take America to become dead land, such as parts of China and Mesopotamia—dead land where nothing grows?

### Much Erosion Is Man-Made

Most of this loss of eroded land is due to man's mistakes and carelessness. He has cut the timber completely off slopes that should have been lumbered more carefully, or not at all. Without protection, the soil has been washed from the rocks by the rain. Trees cannot grow on bare rocks, nor can rocks hold water, so as the years went on the gullies on the slopes were cut deeper and deeper.

Meadows were burned on purpose, by land-owners, and forests by accident. The burning killed the organic life in the topsoil, burned the humus, and set the stage for erosion.

Farmers placed too much livestock in their fields. Instead of putting three or four cows on a small piece of land, they pastured twenty or more. The cattle ate all the ground cover, and packed the earth so hard that the rain could not sink in but ran off the surface, washing the dirt with it (*See Grassland under Grass*).

Too many farmers plowed their fields *up and down* the slopes instead of *across* the slopes. The rainwater rushed through the furrows and carried much of the valuable topsoil with it to the bottom of the hill. In some places gullies of tremendous proportions developed after a few years and hardly a thing would grow on the poor soil left exposed.

The practice of growing the same crop year after year on the same piece of ground and not alternating with a cover crop that would return nourishment to the earth, soon exhausted the soil to the point where it often washed away easily.

### Dust Storms and Floods

Erosion of a field here and a hillside there seldom caused much comment. The process was a gradual one that went on unnoticed except by the farmer who found, sonner or later, that he could no longer grow a paying crop on his land. But when newspapers carried stories of dust storms and great floods, this was big news, for it often meant the lives of many people. These catastrophies were called acts of God, over which man had no control. A few people knew otherwise. They could clearly trace these events to the eroded fields and hillsides. The rain fell, and instead of soaking into the ground, was, carried away into the little brooks whose banks could not always hold the unnatural rush of water. Erosion had set in there, too—and so on into the big rivers. Instead of wandering slowly toward the sea, the water rushed down in a hurry. Great floods were caused by too much water reaching the same place all at once. When the drier months came, the water was gone prematurely from the little brooks and streams. They

became dry and the soil parched. On the Great Plains the powdery, exhausted soil was whipped into the air by hot summer winds and literally whole farms were blown away.

### The Soil Conservation Service

The land was sick, but a cure was sought. A bureau of the United States Department of Agriculture was formed, called the Soil Conservation Service. Many of the men in the service were technicians who tirelessly studied the problem of soil destruction and the remedies. They planted hundreds of millions of trees on eroded slopes, sloped and planted thousands of shifting gullies, and showed farmers how to plan the land's use so that little or no soil should be lost. They did not forget about wildlife. Recognizing that wildlife is dependent on the soil and the soil, in turn, upon wildlife, a wildlife division was included in the Soil Conservation Service.

If one wishes further information in soil conservation he should write to the Soil Conservation Service (Education Section), United States Department of Agriculture, Washington, D.C. —R.T.P.

#### Recommended Reading

**Deserts on the March**—Paul B. Sears. Simon and Schuster, New York.

**Rich Land, Poor Land**—Stuart Chase. McGraw-Hill, New York.

**The Land Renewed: The Story of Soil Conservation**—William R. Van Dersal and Edward H. Graham. Oxford University Press, New York.

**Land and Wildlife**—Edward H. Graham. Oxford University Press, New York.

**Save the Soil**—Cornell Rural School Leaflet, Vol, 29, No 4. Cornell University, Ithaca, New York.

**Soil Conservation**—A magazine issued monthly by the Soil Conservation Service of the United States Department of Agriculture, Washington, D.C.

**The Wasted Land**—Gerald Johnson. University of North Carolina Press, Chapel Hill, North Carolina.

**Soil Erosion a National Menace**—Circular No. 33, United States Department of Agriculture. Superintendent of Documents, Government Printing Office, Washington, D.C.

*Townsend's solitaire is usually seen singly except during migration*

## SOLITAIRE
**Townsend's Solitaire**
**Other Common Names**—None
**Scientific Name**—*Myadestes townsendi*
**Family**—Turdidae (thrushes, solitaires, and bluebirds)
**Order**—Passeriformes
**Size**—Length, 8 to 9½ inches
**Range**—Mountain country, Sierra Nevada and Rocky Mountains, from Alaska and Canada almost to Mexico

### Habits of the Townsend's Solitaire

No one seems able to describe the solitaire in appearance or action without making it a composite bird, running the gamut from the robin to the catbird, mockingbird, phoebe, flycatcher, thrasher, wood thrush, and bluebird. One could add several more, such as the dovelike stretching of its neck, and the peering over its shoulder, cuckoowise. In the fluttering feeding, it has the spread-tail appearance of the scissortailed flycatcher or of a large humming-bird whirring its wings while gathering food. And yet, no bird is more distinctly itself than the modest self-sufficient solitaire. In 1840 John James Audubon named and sketched the Townsend's solitaire from a single female specimen collected near the Columbia River by his friend, J.K. Townsend, a pioneer American naturalist. The relationship of the solitaire to other birds was then somewhat of an ornithological puzzle, but the solitaire is now known to belong to the thrush family.

The Townsend's solitaire is usually a lone bird except during its fall migration from the mountains to lower areas when it is sometimes with its fellows in small groups, though some observers have reported flocks numbering hundreds. Bitterly cold weather at Yellowstone National Park has been known to bring together the solitaire, snipe, raven, mallard, and other birds, all warming themselves in the steam heat issuing from the warm springs.

Often the solitaire seems to completely ignore the presence of a human being, yet a pause in feeding, the quiver and nervous folding of wings—definitely thrush style—usually foretell the sudden take-off with its wonderfully free and rapid flight.

Though the solitaire's nest is typical of thrush and robin nests, mud is not used in its construction. The nest is loosely made of twigs and almost any trashy debris and lined with finer grasses, moss, or pine needles. An overflow apron, or "porch," frequently betrays its location on the ground, or under an old stump or boulder, or in a cavity in a bank close to a stream or waterfall. On Mt. Shasta, in California, the nest is often found under the roots of some tall fir with snowbanks close by, and it has been found elsewhere up to 12,000 feet on bare slopes with granite knobs exposed. Cutbanks are also adopted as nesting sites. In Idaho, to save a nest in jeopardy during a roadblasting job, men scooped the fledglings and all into a hat until an overhang within six feet of the site was demolished. They replaced the nest and soon the hungry youngsters were being fed again by the devoted parents.

Through a binocular, the solitaire's eyes look as big and bright as old-fashioned shoebuttons, but they hold a limpid softness. At close range the solitaire's eye-ring shows uniformly heavy; otherwise one receives the impression of more ring at the rear of the eye.

Although guileless in its roosting and nesting, the solitaire, is not usually taken in banding station traps; however, at Florence Lake, California, a birdbander dropped a hat over a juvenile, and that one did wear a band (See Bird-banding under Bird).

Solitaires supplement their berry diet in winter with a moth or two. They also guard their winter feeding areas against other birds. A female red-bellied woodpecker may come "chuffing" in to feed on the solitaire's cedar berries; less often, a yellow-shafted flicker. But on an overcast February day a flock of cedar waxwings may move into the solitaire's territory. As they shift about, the solitaire may burst on them like a little gray bomber and drive them from his cedars. These forays are carried out by the solitaire with dash and verve, with a lovely display of white-flanked tail and flailing windmill wings.

In 1939 C.W. Lockerbie, an ornithologist of Salt Lake City, returning from a Utah canyon, saw a flock of Bohemian waxwings settling in the haw thicket in which a solitaire fed. The bird dashed from one to another, chasing them about from place to place. Finally they all congregated in the tops of an adjacent oak clump. Though the waxwings raised their crests and trilled, the solitaire charged them and drove them down the canyon. Another time Lockerbie observed a quite different reaction. Hearing an unrecognized gnatcatcherlike distress call, he discovered it came from a solitaire watching a Bohemian waxwing that was caught in a rose bramble. After releasing the waxwing and placing it in a snow hollow with rose hips (red fruits of the rose) that he provided for the injured bird, he saw no more of the solitaire. Both waxwing and most of the rose hips were gone the next day.
—E.L.R.

*Recommended Reading*

**Life Histories of North American Thrushes, Kinglets, and Their Allies**—A.C. Bent. (Paperback) Dover Publications, Inc., New York.

## SOLOMON'S SEAL
**Other Common Names**—Sealwort
**Scientific Name**—*Polygonatum biflorum*
**Family**—Liliaceae (lily family)
**Range**—Florida to Texas, north to Connecticut, New York, southern Ontario, southern Michigan, Illinois, Iowa, and Nebraska
**Habitat**—Dry to moist, sandy, loamy or rocky woods and thickets

*Solomon's seal*

**Time of Blooming**—May through late June

The *biflorum* used in the scientific name of this plant refers to the fact that two yellowish-green flowers hang from the axils of each leaf. The two slender stems of the flowers are united where they are attached to the main stalk. In Latin *bi* mean *two* and *florum* refers to the *flower*.

The *seal* is derived from the fact that the scars on the underground rootstalk, or stem, resemble the seal used in ancient days. The Solomon's seal has only one growing point—at the tip of the rootstalk. Each year the growth made during the summer dies back to the underground stalk, and leaves a scar that is not lost when the plant starts to grow the following spring. As the underground stem is usually not buried very deeply it is possible to pull the earth to one side and count the "seals" and tell something of the age of the plant. It may live 15 or more years.

The long, slender, nodding flower stalk may reach a height of four feet while its close relative, the giant Solomon's seal, sometimes grows to a height of eight feet and usually has three flowers hanging from the axils of the leaves. The flowers are attractive to bumblebees and may be cross-pollinated by these visitors.

The Solomon's seal is not an abundant species in many parts of its range and is listed on the wildflower conservation lists in many states. (*See also False Solomon's Seal; and under Wildflower Protection*)

## SORA
**Other Common Names**—Carolina rail, railbird, crake
**Scientific Name**—*Porzana carolina*
**Family**—Rallidae (rails, gullinules, and coots)
**Order**—Gruiformes
**Size**—Length, 8½ inches
**Range**—North America. Breeds in northern half of the United States northward to central British Columbia, southern Mackenzie and Gulf of St. Lawrence. Winters from northern California, Illinois, southward through West Indies to northern South America

This species is easily distinguished from the Virginia rail, the only other North American rail that resembles it in size, by its short yellowish bill and, in the adult, by the black on the throat and face.

The sora's favorite haunts are wet meadows and freshwater marshes in general, also brackish marshes near the seacoast. It may occasionally dwell far

*Sora*

## SOURIS NATIONAL WILDLIFE REFUGE

[Editor's Note: Lower Souris, Upper Souris, and Des Lacs National Wildlife Refuges are in the Souris River Watershed of North Dakota. The two Souris Refuges are on the Souris River; Des Lac is a refuge on a tributary of that name. The three refuges were established by Congress in 1935 when they were added to the national wildlife refuge system to provide resting, breeding, and feeding grounds for waterfowl, and a sanctuary for prairie chickens and sharptail grouse. The following account of the Lower Souris Refuge was written by C. J. Henry, Refuge Manager.]

*Summer On The Souris Marsh*

The Lower Souris National Wildlife Refuge lies in the heart of America's duck cradle—the ancestral nesting grounds of the waterfowl. Each spring since the beginning of time the migratory birds have rushed back in eager haste, spreading over the land to perform the all-vital function of reproduction; in the autumn vast hordes have gathered to rest and feed before hastening southward ahead of the beginning of winter. Before their drainage for agriculture about 1918, the Souris marshes were unsurpassed as a haven for marshbirds, and the tales by the early settlers of these concentrations of waterfowl are almost more than the mind can grasp.

Because of its isolated geographical position, this locality was not settled until comparatively recent times. The early historical records are scanty as most of the early exploring expeditions followed the course of the Missouri River or its tributaries and missed the Souris country entirely.

The Souris, or Mouse, River, originates in Canada, flows south into North Dakota, thence back into Canada, finding its ultimate destiny in the waters of Hudson Bay. This locality was touched

from marshes about springs or grassy runs of upland meadows. The sora, like all rails, is shy and secretive and succeeds in eluding its pursuers by rapidly slipping away through the reeds or grasses. When forced to take flight its efforts seem weak and feeble, yet it succeeds in making long migratory journeys.

The sora is a favorite gamebird and, in former times, was killed in large numbers. In New England it is especially abundant during the autumnal migrations and is hunted along the tidal lagoons that thread the salt marshes. Its food consists of small crustaceans, insects, worms, and seeds of wild grasses.

The nest is of grasses and weeds, in or near marshes. From 6 to 16 buff-colored eggs, spotted with reddish-brown, are laid.

*Souris National Wildlife Refuge, North Dakota, offers protection to mammals such as these raccoons*

briefly by a few early explorers and trappers, followed by the cattle ranchers, and then the homesteaders, all lured by tales of the fabulous fertility of the great rolling plains. The first eminent ornithologist to visit the region was Dr. Elliot Coues, an Army surgeon, who left excellent records of his studies there in the 1870's, and a vivid picture of the wealth of birdlife when he wrote, "Often as we lay encamped on the Mouse River, the stillness of the midnight would be broken by the hoarse, rattling croaks of the cranes coming overhead, the noise finally dying in the distance, to be succeeded by the shrill pipe of numberless waders, the honking of geese, and the whistle of the pinions of myriads of wild fowl that shot past, sounding to the sleepy ears like the rushing sound of a far away locomotive."

Never again, unless man destroys himself, will there be such untold numbers of marshbirds, and even now some are gone forever. The inevitable result of the rapid expansion of the nation was the decimation of wildlife populations; it is as futile to deplore this loss as to mourn the passing of the long extinct, fossil bird, Archaeopteryx.

The decline of the Souris marshes reflects the well-known story—wanton slaughter of the wildfowl, and then drainage. As the life-giving waters were sucked away by the drainage ditches, the countless clouds of marshbirds melted away. But, as with many such ill-conceived drainage projects, this one, too, proved to be unworthy of the cost. The soil was too heavy for the growing of grain crops and most of the meadows became too dry to sustain the stands of wild hay.

Restoration of the marshes was started in 1935 by the Fish and Wildlife Service, United States Department of the Interior, and was accomplished by the construction of a series of dams at regular intervals throughout the valley. The flood waters of the Souris were impounded to restore the parched lowlands once more to nature's original design. Present management with regulated water levels and protection has reestablished conditions that are likely more attractive than in the heyday of the marshes before the advent of the white man.

As one moves in a duck boat across the marsh, the green and black of the timber looms nearer. Directly to the south across the gleaming marsh the sand hills rise to rival the beauty of the summer sky. How different the picture must have been when these hills were shifting dunes lashed by the waves of an ancient glacial lake. Just beyond the refuge boundary, a farm tractor chugs serenely about the task of turning up the rich prairie soil. White streamers waver and flutter behind—Franklin's gulls eagerly snatch up the insects, grubs, and mice dispossessed by the plow, food for the young gulls in the tremendous nesting colonies. Far above, a horde of white pelicans ride an updraft high into the heavens, banking and soaring on

*Cormorants cluster several nests in each tree in Souris National Wildlife Refuge, North Dakota*

motionless pinions; soon they are mere specks in the sky, now white, now black, as they float in lazy circles. The sounds of the great marsh blend into a tremendous symphony. The calls of five species of grebes penetrate the din of gabbling ducks and screaming terns, punctuated by the very voice of the prairie marsh—the indescribable song of the yellow-headed blackbird. A prairie marsh wren scolds nervously from an adjacent patch of rushes, while the delightful tinkling of the bobolinks carries from a distant meadow.

And now the boat enters the trees where the river wends its sinuous course through dead stands of timber, finally gliding to lazy rest among the reeds and rushes of the marsh. The Souris is an ancient stream of glacial origin, replete with sloughs and oxbows, that feels its tortuous way through a land once the home of the Indian. Of his contemporaries, the beaver, the red-tailed hawk, and the deer remain—the Indian has gone along with the buffalo.

There is but little doubt that there are at present many more deer in the refuge area than in the era of the Indian. With competition gone and their natural enemies eliminated or reduced to a mere fragment, they have multiplied at an astounding pace. Without careful and calculated management the refuge deer herd would long since have destroyed itself, carrying with it to destruction the food supply of itself and many of its associates.

In the quiet solitude of the partly flooded forest, the observer sits quietly admiring the grace of the swallows and the precision of the flycatchers. From the cool dark gloom the ethereal song of the willow thrush, or veery, belittles

*In handsome summer plumage, the horned grebe is one of five species of grebes to nest in Souris National Wildlife Refuge, North Dakota*

*The photograph (above) shows the Souris marshes from the south end*

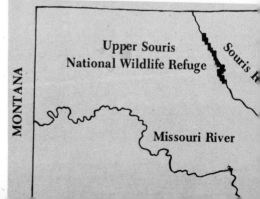

the efforts of its neighbors. There the naturalist finds many birds common to a similar habitat in the East—the chickadee, the hairy woodpecker, the downy woodpecker, the nuthatch, the screech owl, and the great horned owl—all permanent residents, and all enjoying the hospitality of the stately elms. There one sees the catbird, robin, and thrasher; the phoebe and the pewee; the familiar red-eyed and warbling vireos; the yellow warbler, the redstart, and the ovenbird; and even the effervescent house wren. From a dense osier tangle comes the cheery melody of the song sparrow.

If there may be disappointment in finding only familiar birds it is compensated for by the discovery of a formidable mass of sticks in the center of a distorted old oak. This is a characteristic magpie nest, completely roofed over, with an entrance hole on one side. Inspec-

tion of the interior is rewarded by the discovery of five youngsters almost full grown, counterparts of the old birds except for shorter tails. A parent scolds from a thorn-apple thicket at a discreet distance.

The boat has now traveled from the wooded river bottom back into the marsh where one is suddenly transported into a world in which the horizons seem infinite. Miles away a farm grove shimmers in the purple haze, assuming the proportions of a major city, while sounds are mellowed by the distance. On the marsh, the naturalist is dazed by the wealth of birdlife—birds of every size, of varied color, and of many voices. Entire islands appear to expand as masses of loafing ducks take to the water as the boat appears. Miniature flotillas of ducklings and goslings hurry hither and yon, escorted and guided by their ever-

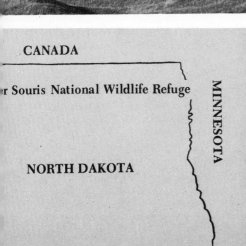

CANADA

Souris National Wildlife Refuge

MINNESOTA

NORTH DAKOTA

*On a tiny island of about half an acre in Souris National Wildlife Refuge, North Dakota, 160 ducks nested. Over 90 per cent of these were gadwalls*

solicitous elders. Coots spatter over the surface in great confusion. An oar, dropped noisily in the boat, raises a petulant chorus of rail calls, and sends a kingfisher rattling on its way.

A small island invites one to get out and stretch his legs. The boat is beached amidst a bewildering clamor of screaming, diving terns. Ducks flutter from the weeds at almost every step, some flapping over the surface in pretended injury, while others fly off to join their mates, each in his jealously guarded domain. One must choose each footstep carefully to avoid the nests of ducks and terns. And what a contrast in nesting customs—the terns choosing the more exposed locations, while the ducks are as secretive as possible.

The duck nests average about ten eggs to the nest, each well protected by a blanket of soft down; nearby the terns have set up housekeeping in a tiny depression outlined by a pitiful collection of knickknacks such as pebbles or pieces of weed stalks, with only two or three eggs in each. Here is an illustration of an evolutionary adjustment of the differences in mortality rates—ducks must bring off big families to offset the tremendous inroads of predators, as they are a highly desirable food item. On the other hand the tern is alert and elusive, so its reproductive capacity need not be so high. Nature has had her troubles and has made her mistakes, but up to the time of civilized man, she was well able to keep matters in hand.

Subsequent investigations reveal that the island, approximately a half acre in size, is highly important to refuge birdlife by providing space for more than 418 nests: at least 250 common terns, 2 ring-billed gulls; 6 red-winged blackbirds, and 160 ducks, of which more than 90 percent are gadwalls. Apparently there is not a single mammal present, and not a bird smaller than the redwing.

To the east the horizon is broken by a tiny group of flooded elms a mile from the nearest mainland. Closer investigation reveals that every possible space in the trees is occupied by a mass of sticks, and almost every mass is filled to overflowing with black, reptilelike cormorants.

There is much activity as the old birds return to the nests laden with the spoils of their fishing expeditions, announcing their return with weird guttural gruntings. How strange that a bird normally so quiet should suddenly find its voice. Among the very highest nests are a few of flimsier construction on which are perched a few tall gangling great blue herons. Actually the four overburdened trees are supporting the nests of six heron families and about a hundred of cormorants. One tree, weary of its load, had recently fallen to its final resting place carrying with it a number of active nests. Dead nestlings float in the water while the dried remains of others lie on the nests.

Distance definitely enhances the glamor of a cormorant, or shag, colony. Intimate inspection reveals a squalor rivaled only by that of the human race in the world's worst slums. Everything within range of the nests is generously whitewashed with cormorant excreta, the smell of which, blended with that of the remains of dead fishes, dead birds, and rotten eggs creates a disgustingly offensive odor. The large cormorant nestlings, when alarmed, regurgitate their dinners without hesitation. Food habits studied here reach the greatest simplicity—the naturalist has simply to retrieve the unsavory messes literally tossed at his feet, but at the same time watching out for direct hits upon his person from above.

The entire food brought by the adults to the young cormorants consists of fishes—bullheads up to six inches long. The sight of the voracious young cormorants delving with their bills into the depths of the parental gullet fills the observer with apprehension—surely they would do mortal injury to the patient old shags.

The nest itself consists of a bulky

*Young cormorants, their heads bare and black, peer from their nest in Souris National Wildlife Refuge, North Dakota*

mass of sticks, lined with fragments of weeds, bark, grasses, or feathers, appearing from the ground somewhat similar to the nest of the great blue heron although considerably more substantial. The occupied nests contain an average of about three shaglets each. When first they emerge from the shell it is without a trace of down or feathers on their homely black skins, and the general appearance is much more reptilian than avian. The shaglets are very restless, their heads bob and roll, and the yellow skin of their throats pulsates rapidly as they shuffle continuously to work into the most advantageous positions. They appear unhappy and discontented with their lot, and their doglike yelping can be heard from afar.

One can eat his lunch in the duck boat at a considerable distance, and upwind, from the cormorants with the boat reposing in a patch of sturdy rushes. The double-crested cormorant must surely be

on the increase, at least judging from the numbers of large and well-established colonies to be found in the Great Plains region, most of which were not in existence in the 1930's. It appears likely that the lowest ebb in population of many colonial-nesting birds has passed; the American era of exploitation has of necessity come to a close. Furthermore, the vast system of federal, state, and private refuges established in the 1930's had begun to provide a series of havens for many forms of wildlife, often for those other than the ones for which the sanctuaries were primarily intended.

Cormorants have been one of the first to take advantage of the ideal habitat and abundant food available on many of those areas. But even more important, on the Lower Souris Refuge they have found freedom from the prejudices and persecutions of a misinformed minority of the public. Habitat and food are not enough—a well-fed bird is about as vulnerable to the gun as is its undernourished neighbor. But one need not be unduly concerned with the occasional potshot by the fisherman who wishes to liquidate competition, or with the hunter who kills for fun or by mistake. The normal habits of the stolid birds are such that they usually stay out of harm's way except during the summer. The rigid protection of nesting colonies should easily insure the perpetuation of the fish-eaters (*See Fish-eating Birds; and under Wildlife: The Wildlife Community*).

The boat has moved again and has worked slowly to the nearest mainland shore where one can again stretch his legs, this time in a rolling pasture bordering the marsh. In the tall grasses along the edges of the marsh, the Nelson's sparrows are singing persistently, and from the damp meadow grasses, the wheezes of the Leconte's sparrows seem to come from everywhere. However, the singers are as elusive as mice. Only once does one of the golden, stubby birds show itself, darting into the air in quick flight only to pitch back in great haste.

An immaculate avocet (*see Avocet*) darts about the shallows, marbled godwits and willets raise a terrific din as though trying to drown out every other noise, frequently punctuating their clamor with a dive at the man in the boat. Killdeers join in the hubbub, and a Swainson's hawk wheels above the scene as it sails in lazy circles almost in the clouds. The ubiquitous blackbirds add their bit to the symphony, although the feeble squeak of the Brewer's blackbird is an exceedingly poor contrast to the song of the redwings (*See under Blackbird*). As one sloshes through the shallow border pools the Wilson's phalaropes join in with their excited grunts that rise to fever pitch when one of their nests is discovered (*See under Phalarope*). This consists of a simple cradle of grasses, but with the typical four-leaf clover arrangement of the eggs.

The song of the Baird's sparrow leads one up to a gently rolling short grass prairie where a small colony of Sprague's pipits is discovered. The males circle and sing on fluttering wings high above the earth, only to suddenly appear on the ground, striding sedately and quietly among the tufts of grass. Grasshopper sparrows and upland sandpipers share the mosquito-infested pasture, along with an alert sharp-tailed grouse, a pair of chestnut-collared longspurs, and a number of flickertails (Richardson's ground squirrels). From a nearby patch of silverberry a gaudy pheasant, with ear tufts erect, crows stridently and in harsh contrast to the glorious burst of music from the western meadowlark. Clay-colored sparrows buzz from every patch of brush.

But it has now grown late, and as one hurries back to the boat, squadrons of night herons appear high in the sky, flapping methodically towards the fishing grounds (*See under Heron*). Ducks speckle the glassy surface as far as the eye can see, and the soul-stirring call of a wild goose rings out from the depths of the marsh. Clouds of gulls beat their way patiently over the meadows, rising and falling in serpentine manner at the dictates of the air currents. The peace of evening has fallen, slackening the tempo of life.

The fame of man as the spoiler is oft and loud acclaimed. But in Lower Souris Refuge, like a gleaming jewel, slumbers the vast marsh. It mirrors the glories of the prairie sunset, an example of a place where man has lifted a hand to restore what he had once destroyed.    —C.J.H.

## SPARROW

The word sparrow is a very old one in the English language and was applied originally to the common yard bird of the Mediterranean basin, one of a large tribe of African weaver birds, *Passer domesticus*.

This is the bird we call the English sparrow, or more properly the house sparrow. It was introduced here by man about 1850 and has since spread across the nation. A close relative, the European tree sparrow *Passer montanus*, was introduced near St. Louis, Missouri, in 1870, but did not spread; nonetheless, a small colony persists there to this day.

These two species, which are members of the Old World seed-eaters, the family Ploceidae, are, ironically, the only true sparrows in America, though we have scores of native sparrowlike species of our own.

This confusion of names came about because the early English colonists to America gave the name of sparrow to the small, brownish, seed-eating birds they found here. None of them realized that these little brown birds were of a different lineage which we now know as the New World seed-eaters, and usually classify as a separate family, the Fringillidae.

The ornithologists who study these interrelationships—the taxonomists—tell us that birds like our widespread and familiar song sparrow are members of that group the British call buntings. Unfortunately, we long ago assigned the word bunting to the more colorful of our own New World seed-eaters, birds like the indigo bunting, cardinal, and the rose-breasted grosbeak. It is ironic that the European buntings almost certainly invaded that continent from North America. We gather this from the fact that there are scores of bunting species—which we obstinately call sparrows—in the Americas, but only a few in Europe and Asia.

To complicate matters further, these same taxonomists—or at least some among them, they don't all agree on this —have discovered that birds like the goldfinch, the redpoll, and the evening grosbeak, are a northern finch group that should be classified separately, as members of a sub-family Carduelinae. And *this* group probably invaded North America from Eurasia, because there are more species there than here.

So, if you enjoy words and their use, this is a great game. Any number can play. If you should join the fun it will become even more complicated, but you will learn, in the process, that man has really learned very little, as yet, of nature's ingenuity.

Speaking of nature's ingenuity, you will find, for example, that birds which appear to be related because they look alike in form and color, may turn out to be quite unrelated, genetically speaking. They look alike because nature has molded them to fit a particular niche, or, perhaps more objectively, because they have been "selected" by the evironment in which they now live. By the same token, birds that were ancestrally related may come to look very unalike because they have dispersed themselves into different habitats. This first phenomenon is called evolutionary convergence; the second case is an example of adaptive radiation.

The large tribe of seed-eaters we call sparrows, buntings, and finches, since they are spread around the world in a great variety of environments, is wonderfully illustrative of this evolutionary process.

We must recognize that it is the population that evolves, though it is of course individual variation that provides the basis for that selection process that is at the heart of evolution. If individual differences—and all living things are unique—have survival value, the process of reproduction will accumulate them, since what is involved there is differential reproductive success. And, gradually, these changes mold the population.

The house sparrow, introduced on this continent only a century or so ago, has already developed recognizable different populations. Minor differences, perhaps, but statistically significant ones, and indicative of greater changes to come. In time, this population which now involves millions of individuals—all the product of those original introductions which probably numbered only about 200 birds—can be expected to produce

*A chipping sparrow watches over its hungry offspring*

new species. Having radiated into almost all of America's varied habitats, each of which makes different demands on them, some groups will become reproductively isolated, either through behavioristic, physiological, or anatomical differentiation. When this happens, a new species will have arisen among them, since this is the test of a species: that it be a population of interbreeding individuals which is reproductively isolated from other populations. Creation of species, then, is a slow, continuing process of segretating populations which accumulate differences until they cut themselves off from other related groups.

—R.C.C.

## Chipping Sparrow

**Other Common Names**—Hair-bird, chip-bird, chippy
**Scientific Name**—*Spizella passerina*
**Family**—Fringillidae (grosbeaks, finches, sparrows, and buntings)
**Order**—Passeriformes
**Size**—Length, 5 to 5½ inches
**Range**—Breeds from central Yukon and southeast through Canada and throughout the United States. Winters chiefly in the southern United States, occasionally as far north as Oklahoma, Tennessee, and New Jersey

Of all the sparrows, one of the best known is the chipping sparrow—the little red-capped bird that frequents gardens in summer. It is a slight and dainty creature compared to the larger house sparrow with which it shares the backyard and shade trees.

The chipping sparrow is so characteristic of towns and gardens that it is always a distinct surprise to find a pair living in an opening in the deep woodlands. In the Far West, they are often seen in the pine and fir forests high on the mountain slopes. In New England and in the eastern Canadian provinces they sing their trill in the same spruce forests where the juncos live.

Some of the other members of the modest sparrow clan have more lilting songs. The chippy's efforts can hardly be called musical, though it is a pleasing sound. The song is a dry, rapid chipping, all on one pitch, normally given in multiples of eight. In other words, the rattle is always 8, 16, 24, or 32 notes long. At daybreak in the morning, before it is light enough to see well, the song is very short, made up of only eight notes—a very short buzz, repeated over and over. As the sun climbs over the horizon, flooding the garden with the first long rays, the song becomes longer and louder. Other males sing nearby in slightly different pitches. They each keep their distance, but will defend their territory if it is invaded.

The nest is built on a low branch of a tree, in a dense ornamental bush or evergreen, or in a thick vine. It is a cuplike structure of intricately woven rootlets—a thin-walled little nest lined with hair. The characteristic hair lining must be much more of a problem these days to the chippy, or hairbird, as it is sometimes called, than it was a generation ago before cars took the place of horses. Horsehairs are now difficult to obtain in some places. The three to five eggs are green-blue with small dots and speckles, not white as are the eggs of most other sparrows.

Incubation takes 10 to 12 days and is shared by both the male and the female, but the female usually does most of it. After 9 or 10 days in the nest, the helpless young feather out and are ready to try their wings and wobbly legs. They have streaked breasts, quite unlike their clear-breasted parents, but most of the streaks disappear as the season advances.

The young male birds start to sing a little in August and begin to look more like the adults, except that their heads have a more striped appearance. Even the adult birds change a little, their red caps becoming duller and their general coloration browner. The family groups join up with others to make little

*Field sparrow*

their buzzy songs in the gardens of the northern states, and early in May, those that summer in northern Canada have reached their nesting grounds. —A.B.,Jr.

**Field Sparrow**
**Other Common Names**—Bush sparrow, field chippy, rush sparrow
**Scientific Name**—*Spizella pusilla*
**Family**—Fringillidae (grosbeaks, finches, sparrows, and buntings)
**Order**—Passeriformes
**Size**—Length, 5¼ to 6 inches
**Range**—Nests across northern United States to Quebec and Maine, south to Texas, Louisiana, Mississippi, and Georgia. Winters in East from Massachusetts south to Mexico and west to Kansas, Missouri, Ohio, West Virginia, and southeastern Pennsylvania

This is one of a small group of perhaps half a dozen sparrows that are general favorites with bird lovers. Unlike many members of the family it is easy to identify, both its markings and its song being very distinctive. The bright rufous color above and its whitish underparts, together with a flesh-colored bill, are excellent field marks.

When the first warm days of spring appear, the field sparrow's plaintive trill may be heard rising up from the fields and roadsides and from many an upland pasture. Later in the drowsy summer heat, the same plaintive, tremulous song may be heard floating over the sunburned fields.

The field sparrow is extremely valuable as a destroyer of insect pests.

The nest is built on the ground or in low bushes, of small weed stalks, coarse grasses, and rootlets and is lined with finer grasses and hair. From three to five bluish-white eggs with brown markings are laid.

**Fox Sparrow**
**Other Common Names**—Foxy finch, fox-colored sparrow

flocks that wander about farms and rural areas. By the time the leaves have fallen, most of them have left Canada and the northern parts of the United States, but a few linger on until late October. Traveling by night with the hosts of other migrants, they reach the southern parts of the United States, where, with the song, savannah, and other sparrows, they line the wires along the roadsides or gather in brown weed beds. Some of the western chipping sparrows penetrate quite far into Mexico in their wanderings.

In early March the chippies begin to move north; by April they are singing

*Fox sparrows nest in low bushes, trees, or on the ground*

**Scientific Name**—*Passerella iliaca*
**Family**—Fringillidae (grosbeaks, finches, sparrows, and buntings)
**Order**—Passeriformes
**Size**—Length, 6¾ to 7½ inches
**Range**—Nests from Alaska south through Canada and east to Newfoundland, south on Pacific Coast to northwestern Wash- ington, in mountains to southern Califor- nia, Nevada, Utah, and Colorado. Winters along Pacific Coast from Canada south to northern Baja Califor- nia; also from Utah east to southern Ontario, and south in eastern and central United States to Arizona, Texas, Gulf Coast, and central Florida

This aristocrat among sparrows, on account of its size and unusual markings, is easily distinguished from its relatives. Its rusty, or fox-red color on the upper parts, together with the whitish rust-marked breast make it stand out as a unique member of the sparrow group. As if further to emphasize its outstanding characteristics, nature has endowed it with unusually large feet and claws.

It is largely a ground-feeding bird, spending most of its time scratching among dead leaves for its food. During migration it lives in thickets and briar patches, or in sheltered ravines grown over with thick shrubbery and vines. There on quiet days flocks of these birds may be heard scratching, often in company with juncos or other sparrows. The busy activities of the birds as they send the crisp, dry leaves flying in all directions will at times give the impression that a flock of barnyard fowls had escaped into the woodlands.

The nest is on the ground, or in low trees or bushes, and is constructed of coarse grasses. It is lined with finer material such as hair, mosses, and feathers. From four to five bluish eggs are laid, speckled and blotched with brown.

**House Sparrow**
**Other Common Names**—English sparrow, gamin, tramp, hoodlum
**Scientific Name**—*Passer domesticus*
**Family**—Ploceidae (weaver finches)
**Order**—Passeriformes
**Size**—Length, 5 to 6¼ inches
**Range**—Breeds throughout the United States and all thickly populated areas of the Canadian provinces, as well as parts of Mexico. Winters in same areas, but a few birds undertake a slight southward migration

The story of the house sparrow is a success story. A native of Europe, it now lives over a large part of the world —throughout the United States, much of Canada, Mexico, temperate South America, Australia, New Zealand, southeastern Africa, and the Hawaiian and Philippine islands. Many other birds have been transplanted into foreign lands, but most of them have not thrived because the conditions there were different from those to which they were accustomed.

The house sparrow, being a city bird in Europe, found nothing essentially different about the cities and farms of the United States. The buildings were much the same; there were the same domestic animals, the same plants in the gardens. In 1850 eight pairs were brought from England to Brooklyn. They were kept in a cage through the winter and released the following spring, but the small flock did not survive. The next year a few more were brought in, and these adjusted successfully. In the next 30 years about 20 other shipments were made. It then seemed that people could not get them established soon enough. They admittedly liked to have sparrows around, and they gave, as their main reason for bringing them over, the control of the dropworm, the caterpillar of the snow-white linden moth, which was a very objectionable pest in cities at that time.

The sparrows followed the railroads west; they even rode the boxcars, and before very long were well established on the Pacific Coast. The cities in southern California were among the last to be invaded by the house sparrow. San Diego saw its first house sparrows in 1913. This is probably because the house finch, a bird with similar habits, had already occupied many of the thickly settled parts of the Southwest.

The house sparrow is blamed for much of the disappearance of native birds around cities, but it is quite likely that the development of large cities would affect birds anyway; in fact, this sparrow is about the only one that can tolerate the conditions of many metropolitan areas. Today house sparrows are part of our native avifauna and have adjusted themselves to their surroundings. They do not have melodious songs, only their monotonous chirping, but they do add the only touch of birdlife to many large cities and would be missed if they were gone.

The house sparrow is far less common in the large cities of the East than it was a generation ago. The invention of the automobile has had something to do with this, for it meant that stables with their horses and oats were replaced by garages with their automobiles and gasoline.

The male house sparrow is brown and has a chestnut patch on the back of his neck and a black bib on his throat which the female lacks. In courtship the male hops around the female with his tail spread and wings drooping. The female, in turn, pecks him, and sometimes catches his wing with her beak. This prompts the male to continue his display with greater intensity.

The house sparrow builds a loosely woven nest of straw, rags, and string. Usually it is placed in a bird box, drain spout, or the cornice of a building. In some places house sparrows make their nests in trees. The five or six spotted white eggs take 12 or 13 days to hatch. The young grow rapidly, and as soon as they leave, another brood is started. Sometimes eggs are laid in nests from which the young have not yet gone. Three to four broods a year are very frequent; thus it is not difficult to understand why the house sparrow was able to spread across the country so quickly.

The young birds out of the nest resemble the female, but have faint breast streakings which later disappear. In the late summer they gather in flocks with other house sparrow families and travel about the cities or countryside. A large proportion of their food is grain,

*House sparrows*

but often they eat weed seeds, the little green caterpillars of leaf-eating insects, rose aphids, and Japanese beetles.

In regions where winters are very cold, house sparrows build roosting nests, warmly lined with feathers. They do this in the high mountains. In most places, they huddle during the night in little groups in a dense bush or tree. By fluffing out their feathers, they can hold warm air close to their bodies. Winter is a critical period for them, and when food is scarce and temperatures low, they often die in large numbers. A.B.,Jr.

**Lark Sparrow**
**Other Common Names**—Quailhead, road-bird, little meadowlark
**Scientific Name**— *Chondestes grammacus*
**Family**—Fringillidae (grosbeaks, finches, sparrows, and buntings)
**Order**—Passeriformes
**Size**—Length, 5½ to 6½ inches

**Range**—Nests from western Oregon and southern British Columbia across southern Canada to Minnesota, Wisconsin, and Michigan, to western New York and central Pennsylvania, and from southern California to Texas, Louisiana, and central Alabama.    Rarely to Virginia and North Carolina.    Winters from central California to Arizona, Texas, and southern Florida

This large, handsome sparrow is a common resident of the Mississippi Valley region, where it is widely distributed in suitable localities. It readily may be distinguished from other sparrows by its bright reddish-brown ear coverts, which, combined with its black-and-white face, give it unusual distinction. Its outstanding field mark, however, is the large amount of white in the tail feathers which is not found to so great an extent in any other sparrow.

In agricultural sections its favorite haunts are upland pastures and scraggly, eroded hillsides. It also lives along roadsides and in fields and orchards. In more sparsely settled sections it occurs in open badlands and sagebrush flats. In such situations it enlivens the lonely spaces with its spritely ways and sweet, lilting song. After the nesting season it often may be seen in small flocks wandering about the countryside.

The nest is of dried grasses and plant stems, on the ground or in low trees or bushes. The eggs are from three to six, white or bluish-white, and speckled on the large end with black and brown.

## Savannah Sparrow
**Other Common Names**—Ground sparrow, groundbird, savannah bunting
**Scientific Name**—*Passerculus sandwichensis*
**Family**—Fringillidae (grosbeaks, finches, sparrows, and buntings)
**Order**—Passeriformes
**Size**—Length, 5¾
**Range**—Nests from Alaska south into

*Savannah sparrow*

Canada, east to Labrador, south to Maryland, West Virginia, Ohio, Indiana, Missouri. Winters in East from Massachusetts south to Central America, and in West from British Columbia, Nevada, and Utah to central New Mexico, Oklahoma, and northern Gulf states

Although possessing no distinctive field marks as some other members of the family, the savannah sparrow may be identified by its striped breast which lacks a central spot, the yellow line in front of the eye, and also by its song that is a faint insectlike ditty somewhat resembling that of the grasshopper sparrow. Its favorite haunts are low, damp meadows and wastelands, where it often occurs in considerable numbers. It is almost mouselike in its habits as it creeps through the grass, invisible to such intruders as may enter its retreat. Its secretive habits make it a rather inconspicuous bird. It occurs, however, in great numbers, particularly during migration, when it is often seen in company with other migrating sparrows.

The savannah sparrow is invaluable as a destroyer of insects, and has been proven to be the greatest eater of beetles of any member of the family.

The nest is on the ground, of grasses or mosses and is lined with finer material or hair. The eggs are four to five, bluish-white, and thickly spotted with reddish-brown.

## Song Sparrow

**Other Common Names**—Silver tongue, everybody's darling, groundbird, red grass-bird, swamp finch
**Scientific Name**—*Melospiza melodia*
**Family**—Fringillidae (grosbeaks, finches, sparrows, and buntings)
**Order**—Passeriformes
**Size**—Length, 5 to 6-¾ inches
**Range**—Breeds from Gulf of St. Lawrence across to Alaska, south to California, Arizona, New Mexico, Missouri, and east to South Carolina. Winters from southern Canada to the Gulf of Mexico

The song sparrow is probably the most common and most widespread of the sparrows. It lives wherever there are meadows or fields with brushy edges, its loose-jointed tail bobbing up and down as it flies from bush to bush. It can always be identified by the large spot in the center of the breast where the brown streaks run together.

Scientists recognize at least 30 different races. Some, such as those in the Aleutian Islands, in Alaska, are very large—nine inches from bill to tail. Those that live in the wet regions of the north Pacific Coast, where the rainfall is over 90 inches a year, are very dark and sooty. Those that live on the dry Colorado Desert in California, where the rainfall is only six inches a year, are very pale and washed out, and blend with the color of the desert sand. There are all degrees between these extremes.

California alone claims 11 types of song sparrows. The song sparrow, wherever it lives is a true North American bird that can adapt itself to wet or dry, hot or cold and is everywhere in harmony with nature.

In the colder parts of the United States and Canada, the song sparrow is a spring bird, as much a herald of spring as the robin or the bluebird. Even in places where they have spent the winter months in obscurity, they become suddenly noticeable during the warmer days of February and early March, when their bright songs cheer up the bleak landscape. The song usually starts with two or three repeated notes followed by a buzz and ending with a trill.

The male song sparrow fights for the portion of pasture or garden that is to be his territory. He takes no part in the building, incubation, or the brooding of the young, but spends most of his time singing from a bush top and chasing birds that come near this territory.

The nest is usually built on the ground, in a clump of grass, or at the base of a bush. If some roaming animal discovers the nest and eats the eggs, the birds will build again. If this attempt also fails, a third try is made. These later nests are often built in bushes or shrubbery off the ground where they are probably safer. The first nest of a young female is just as well made as the ones she builds later.

The three to five white eggs, spotted with brown, take about two weeks to hatch. The female broods the eggs and has to slip off every 20 or 30 minutes to get food or water. The song sparrow usually has two broods a season. Like other birds, they will succeed if they are not discovered by predators and if there is plenty of food. When the undergrowth is cut out, or trimmed the way it is in some city parks, finding food becomes a problem, and the birds eventually disappear.

Two-thirds of the song sparrow's food

*Adult song sparrows can be identified by a brown spot on their chests*

is vegetable matter—weed seeds and berries. The other third is made up of insects.

In the colder parts of their range song sparrows are migratory, but a few spend the winter as far north as parts of southern Canada. They are more solitary at this season than most other sparrows, but will join the other birds that come to the feeding stations around the house.            —A. B., Jr.

**Swamp Sparrow**
**Other Common Names**— Swamp song sparrow
**Scientific Name**—*Melospiza georgiana*
**Family**—Fringillidae (grosbeaks, finches, sparrow, and buntings)
**Order**—Passeriformes
**Size**—Length, 5 to 5¾ inches
**Range**—Nests across southern Canada and northern United States from British Columbia to Newfoundland, south to Missouri and north to Nebraska. Winters from Nebraska and Wisconsin to Massachusetts and south to Florida, Gulf Coast, and Texas

This species is somewhat smaller than its relative, the song sparrow, but may readily be distinguished from it by the lack of streakings on the breast, which is plain grayish, whitening in the center and on the throat. Its call note and song are likewise quite distinct from those of the song sparrow. The call note of this species more closely resembles the sharp metallic *clink* of the white-throated sparrow than the softer, more nasal *chirp* of the song sparrow. The swamp sparrow's song, although consisting of a succession of sweet notes, has little of the quality of variations of that of the song sparrow.

It is a timid and retiring bird and seldom ventures far from the sedges and reeds which are its favorite haunts. When flushed in its swampy retreats, it flits with nervous haste and drops out of sight in some tussock or among the thick sedges from where it is with difficulty dislodged again.

*Swamp sparrow*

The nest is on the ground, of coarse grasses, rootlets, and leaves. The eggs are four to five, bluish-white, and finely speckled with rufous brown.

**Tree Sparrow**
**Other Common Names**—Snow chippy, winter chip bird, Canada sparrow
**Scientific Name**—*Spizella arborea*
**Family**—Fringillidae (grosbeaks, finches, sparrows, and buntings)
**Order**—Passeriformes
**Size**—Length, 6 to 6½ inches
**Range**—Nests from Alaska south through Canada east to Quebec and Labrador. Winters from southern Canada south to California, east to Texas and North Carolina

This interesting member of the sparrow family may be readily distinguished from its relatives by its reddish crown and the solitary blackish-brown spot in the center of its breast.

*Tree sparrows are red-crowned birds and have a tiny spot on their breasts*

*The vesper sparrow nests on the ground in cultivated fields and pastures*

In midautumn it appears in our northern states, often with juncos and, as winter comes on, it flocks in scattered companies over the snow-clad fields.

Like the junco, the tree sparrow frequents the thicket-bordered edges of woodlands, old fencerows overgrown with vines and briars, and especially weedy fields. It also comes to gardens and often shares the feeding-shelf with chickadees, nuthatches, and juncos.

As a weed-seed feeder, the tree sparrow probably has no equal. The ornithologist F.E.L. Beal, estimated that this little winter sojourner consumes over 800 tons of weed seeds each season in Iowa alone. If this is true of the state of Iowa, enormous quantities must be eaten throughout its entire winter range.

The nest is usually on the ground but sometimes is built in low bushes. There are four or five eggs of a pale greenish-blue, speckled with brown.

**Vesper Sparrow**
**Other Common Names** — Bay-winged bunting, grass finch, pasture bird
**Scientific Name** — *Pooecetes gramincus*
**Family** — Fringillidae (grosbeaks, finches, sparrows, and buntings)
**Order** — Passeriformes
**Size** — Length, 5½ to 6½ inches
**Range** — Nests from British Columbia across southern Canada to Quebec and Nova Scotia south to Missouri, Tennessee, and North Carolina, and from western Oregon to central California, east to Nevada, Utah, Colorado, Arizona, and New Mexico to Missouri. Winters from central California, southern Great Basin and Rocky Mountains east to Illinois, southern Pennsylvania and Connecticut, south to southern Baja California, Mexico, and Gulf Coast to central Florida

When the cold and sodden fields have begun to show a first faint tinge of green, the vesper sparrow returns to pastures and roadsides. There is no difficulty in distinguishing it from other members of the family, for as it flies, its trade-mark in the form of white outer tail feathers can be so plainly seen that all doubt as to its identity are at once settled.

The vesper sparrow, like the meadowlark, is in a special way a pastoral bird and is associated in our minds with life on the farm. When the plowman turns his first furrow in the spring, this little bird is already present, running and flitting about the fields and gleaning among the winter-frayed stubble. When seeding-time arrives its sweet plaintive song may be heard from field and roadside, floating out on the quiet air. It is one of the farmer's best friends, for it destroys large numbers of insects that are injurious to fruit and crops, as well as many noxious weed seeds.

The nest is on the ground in open pastures or cultivated fields. It is a slight affair of coarse grasses lined with finer materials. The eggs are from four to five and bluish-white, speckled with reddish-brown.

**White-crowned Sparrow**
**Other Common Names** — White-crown
**Scientific Name** — *Zonotrichia leucophrys*
**Family** — Fringillidae (grosbeaks, finches, sparrows, and buntings)
**Order** — Passeriformes
**Size** — Length, 6½ to 7½ inches
**Range** — Nests from Alaska south across Canada to Labrador and Newfoundland, south in the western United States to California, east to Nevada, Arizona, and New Mexico. Winters from southern British Columbia to Baja California, east to Wyoming, Kansas, Missouri, Kentucky, and Maryland, south to northern Florida and Texas and Mexico

This handsome, aristocratic-looking crowned sparrow is a nesting bird of the cool, brushy environments of the subarctic and the alpine regions of the western mountains, as well as the northern Pacific coast. In this broad range it is subdivided into three subspecies. The Pacific coast race is resident but the eastern birds winter chiefly in the brushy field borders of the southern interior. Many are killed in California's truck garden region, but it is still a very common bird whose plaintive, wheezy song is heard everywhere.

*The white-crowned sparrow is a brilliantly marked member of the sparrow group*

*The song of the white-throated sparrow is well-known in the coniferous forests of the North*

**White-throated Sparrow**
**Other Common Names**—Peabody bird, Canada bird, whitethroat
**Scientific Name**—*Zonotrichia albicollis*
**Family**—Fringillidae (grosbeaks, finches, sparrows, and buntings)
**Order**—Passeriformes
**Size**—Length, 6½ to 7 inches
**Range**—Nests in spruce belt in Canada east to Newfoundland and south to New England, New York, and Pennsylvania, west to British Columbia. Winters from southern New England south to northern Florida and Gulf Coast west to northern California, north to southern Canada

The white-throated sparrow is quite a handsome bird. With the exception of the fox sparrow, bird students would perhaps vote it the handsomest species of the eastern states. It is slightly longer than the chipping sparrow, and the chipping sparrow is much more slender.

Of all the many members of the sparrow family inhabiting North America no species is better known for its song than this one. In the evergreen forests of the North its clear, beautiful whistle is one of the most characteristic sounds of the region, and it strikes the ear with a freshness that is truly delightful. Many writers have tried to interpret its song and tell us in English what the bird is saying when it sits upon the pine top and whistles away for half an hour at a time. The call to a Canadian observer strongly suggests the words *Oh see me me me me me*. A very common rendering of its song is given as *Old Sam Peabody, Peabody, Peabody.* There are many variations of the last translation, in all of which the word *Peabody* is prominent; hence, long ago the custom arose of calling it the Peabody bird.

A Nova Scotian variant is Joe Kennedy bird.

It is rather easy to whistle an imitation of the whitethroat's notes, and the bird is so curious that often it will come from a distance in response to the call, and will chirp, look, and crane its neck with the liveliest interest. Comparatively few birds will do this. The bobwhite will come if called by an expert, and in spring or summer almost anyone can gather a number of small birds around one in the woods by merely sucking the back of the hand, thus making a squeaking noise (*See under Bird: Attracing Birds by Sounds*). In this case the birds show evidence of alarm and concern, for such a sound is a fair imitation of a baby bird in distress.

In the fall of the year white-throated sparrows consume many berries, which they pick off the vines and berry-producing trees. They also collect the seeds of those berries that, dried or decayed, fall to the ground.

In eating weed seeds, the birds hop about among the vines or tall weeds and carefully search through the debris on the ground. When the earth is strewn with fallen leaves, and these are dry, the rattling, rustling noise of a flock of feeding whitethroats may lead one to think a grouse family is advancing along the ground. Whitethroats fly up and alight on the sides of ragweeds, and, hanging there, fluttering, they pick at the seeds that have not yet dropped. It may readily be seen that these birds are valuable to the farmer who spends most of his summer trying with hoe and plow to keep the weeds from overrunning his crops. For this reason laws for its protection have been passed in all states where this sparrow is found.

Among migratory birds the exclusive insect-eaters are, as a rule, among the first to leave their northern homes in autumn, while those that are more omnivorous in their feeding usually linger until the winter is fairly upon them. Many of the whitethroats do not depart until November, and, in fact, numerous flocks remain all winter as far north as New Jersey and Ohio. Some indeed, are often seen throughout the winter at places even north of this region. In suitable localities all over the South as far as the Gulf of Mexico they pass the colder months. Here they thrive and grow fat and sometimes are killed and eaten. Audubon described at length the method employed by people in Louisiana to secure the birds in the early part of the last century. They were killed by blowing sharp sticks tipped with squirrel fur through a hollow reed; in short, these hunters used blowguns much like those employed today by Indians in the jungles of South America and elsewhere. Today the laws of all the eastern states protect the whitethroat, and its enemies are now mainly the screech owl, to a lesser extent the sparrow hawk and sharp-shinned hawk, but most of all vagrant house cats.

By the middle of November the majority of these sparrows have departed from the latitude of New York, and will not be seen there again until March or early April. From then until the dogwoods are in full flower these birds are about, and may be seen if one will only take the time to tramp about the country until they are found. They begin to arrive in Canada early in May and soon all over the eastern part of the Dominion, where forests or woodland abound, the whitethroats are to be seen. In the summer they occur as far west as Alberta, and are said to be very common in the central part of that province.

The nest is usually built on or near the ground. It is made of grasses, grapevine stems and other similar substances. The lining is usually of fine grasses, although at times feathers, deer hair, or rabbit fur is used as a soft bed for the eggs. Four or five eggs are laid, and their pale green ground-color is thickly marbled with various shades of chocolate and brown.  —T.G.P.

# SPIDER

Spiders are arthropods, jointed-legged animals closely allied to insects and crustaceans. Within the phylum Arthropoda, they are members of the class Arachnida, along with scorpions, ticks, and mites, which comprise the order Araneida.

All spiders are characterized by their two body segments (cephalothorax and and abdomen) joined by a narrow stalk; by their fangs (chelicerae) that contain the poison glands; by their feelers (pedipalps); and by their four pairs of walking legs.

The tip of the abdomen has protrusions, usually six, called spinnerets, that exude a liquid that dries almost immediately to become the silk with which their webs are made.

Spiders have small mouths, and do not eat solid food. They kill their prey (usually insects, but large tropical species sometimes feed on small vertebrates) by poison, and then suck the juices from the body.

Some species build webs of great complexity; others run a few random lines; others build no web at all but stalk their prey over the ground.

Most species have several simple eyes near the top of the head, as well as large, compound eyes at the front. The larger eyes reflect artificial light at night.
—G.B.S.

## Some Habits of Spiders

Spiders, scorpions, mites, and ticks belong to the class Arachnida. They are sometimes confused with insects (class Insecta, or Hexapoda) but there are many differences between the two classes. One easily remembered difference is the number of walking legs: Insects have six legs; spiders have eight. The female spider lays a mass of eggs around which she spins an egg sac. When the young hatch they shed their skins very soon and are then tiny, perfectly formed spiders. As they grow, they molt a number of times.

Of all our small animal neighbors, spiders have been the most maligned. They are shy little creatures and when disturbed make every effort to hide away. Although all spiders can bite and inject venom, our northern species have very little poison and few of them are strong enough to bite through the human skin. The large hairy tarantula living in the South may inflict a bad bite, but there is only one spider of the northeastern United States, the black widow, that may inflict serious bites to human beings. Spiders are beneficial or useful in their function in nature because of the numbers of insects they eat. Some spiders are sedentary, either trapping their prey by snares or lying in ambush for it; some make use of any available retreat; others, like wolves, stalk their prey; some make silk-lined tunnels in the earth; and some of these burrowing spiders close the entrance with cleverly constructed trapdoors. The student of nature misses a great deal if he fails to observe the interesting habits of spiders in making their homes, catching their prey, and escaping from their enemies.

Glands in the abdomen of the spider produce fluids that harden in the air and form silk. The outlets from these glands are at the end of the abdomen and are called spinnerets. The silk of insects (caterpillars for example, *see under Caterpillar*) comes from their mouths. Spiders use silk to spin snares to trap moths, flies, and others of their prey, to wrap up their masses of eggs, and to line their retreats. Man uses spiders' silk for cross-threads in telescopes. Many spiders make no snare, but catch their prey by stealth, wandering from place to place within a limited area. The webmakers are sedentary, living on or near their webs.

## Common Spiders

The orb weavers (Argiopidae) are the spiders that build the beautiful wheel-shaped webs. The young and some adults build a new web daily, but as a rule

*The poisonous female black widow spider has a red hour glass on the underside*

the web is rebuilt only when it has been partially or entirely destroyed. Sundown is the time favored by spiders for constructing webs. The spider lives on or near its snare for trapping insects, where it can easily rush upon the entangled prey. Most of the web-building species wrap the victim in a sheet of silk and kill it by injecting poison secreted from glands connected with the claws in front of the mouth. The silk-wrapped prey is then eaten. The orange garden spider, *Argiope aurantia,* is black with orange or yellow spots on the back of the abdomen. The beautiful leucauge, *Leucauge venusta,* a bright green-and-silver orb weaver, marked with gold, spins a striking web on shrubs and trees.

The funnel-web spiders (Agelenidae) spin sheetlike webs in the grass and in the corners of barns and cellars. One of our most common spiders is the grass spider, *Agelena naevia.* Its webs may be seen in fields and meadows in the early morning when the dew has condensed on them. At one side of the sheet is a tubular retreat with an opening below to allow the spider to escape.

The comb-footed spiders (Theridiidae) are mostly sedentary. To this family belongs the most common of our house spiders, *Theridion tepidariorum,* the one that builds a tangled web in neglected corners of rooms. The hind legs of these spiders bear combs that assist in throwing liquid silk over insects caught in the web. The black widow, *Latrodectus mactans,* more common in the southern states, also belongs to this family. It is a coal-black spider with red or yellow markings. Its bite is dangerous because the venom is extremely virulent. However, the black widow offers to bite human beings only upon extreme provocation. The filmy dome spider, *Linyphia marginata,* belongs to a family related to the comb-footed spiders and makes a very beautiful web in the grass.

The wolf spiders (Lycosidae) are hunters and stalk their prey, lurking under stones or in their silk-lined burrows.

The females carry the egg sac attached to the spinnerets. When the eggs hatch, the young climb upon their mother's back and are carried about by her for some time. The young cannibals eat each other and any tiny insects they can secure. *Dolomedes tenebrosus,* a large blackish spider of a related family, is common around water and has been known to capture and eat small fishes.

The jumping spiders (Attidae) are small spiders, common on logs, fences, the sides of buildings and on plants. Many species are brightly colored. The jumping spiders are hunters, their short, stout legs enabling them to jump swiftly upon their prey. The Attidae do not make webs, but they do make nests in which to spend the winter, or when molting or laying eggs.

## Spiders and Their Silk

Spiders have long been celebrated for spinning silk from their bodies. The scientific name for the class of animals to which spiders and their kin belong is Arachnida, from the Greek word for spider, *arachne.* It commemorates the name of a Lydian princess who became so expert in the art of weaving that she dared to challenge Athena to a test of skill. Although Arachne's work was faultless, that of the goddess was of a perfection beyond attainment of mere mortals. So humiliated was the rash Arachne that she attempted to hang herself, but the noose was loosened to become a cobweb, and the maiden was changed into a spider and condemned to perpetual spinning. The English word spider is a corruption of *spinder,* one who spins, and the root persists in the words spinstress and spinster, both having reference to women who spin as a profession.

Few people are aware of the great dependence of spiders on silk. Whereas some insects spin silk during the larval stages, the average spider excels as a spinner from shortly after birth until death. The ability to spin is an early gift of the spiderling and is developed after it has accomplished its first molt and before its emergence from the egg sac. Immediately upon leaving the sac it strings out its dragline threads and attaches them at intervals to the substratum. Thereafter it is never free of this securing band throughout its whole life.

The numerous sedentary spiders, the comb-footed spiders, tangle and sheet weavers, orb weavers, and all those that hang back downward from the silken lines of their snares, are so dependent on silk that many have become slaves of their elaborate webs. Within them they are supreme autocrats but when away they are often clumsy, helpless creatures. Sight plays only a small role in their lives but they compensate for their poor eyesight by spinning a more or less expansive web to enlarge their range of perception. The struggles of an insect in remote recesses of the web will send the spider rushing to the site of a prospective meal. Silk is of paramount importance during the whole lifespan for spiders of this type.

Contrasted with these aerialists are many wandering types that run over the ground or vegetation in an upright position and place a smaller degree of reliance on silk. The familiar jumping spiders swarm on the ground in forests and grasslands and find an abundant food supply in the many ground insects. The jumping spiders have become specialists for stalking prey over foliage by means of sharp eyes and the tarsal claw tufts that allow them to climb precipitous surfaces with ease. These big-eyed vagrants use silk chiefly for lining their retreats, covering their eggs, and for spinning their draglines. Their success depends on a body built for strength and swiftness, and ability to perceive, pursue, and capture prey by the chase.

## Spinning the Silk

The spinning organs of spiders are fingerlike appendages called spinnerets, located near the end of the abdomen on the undersurface. These are tipped with

*A banded argiope spins a trap of silk around a grasshopper that has become ensnared in its web*

many tiny spinning tubes and relatively few larger ones called spigots from which the liquid silk issues. The silk is produced within the abdomen in secreting organs, or glands, of which at least seven distinct kinds are known, each producing a different kind of silk.

Thus the spider has at its command various types of silk. The spinnerets are flexible fingers that can be extended, withdrawn, compressed, and manipulated like human hands. The threads are sometimes relatively simple lines in multiples of two, but frequently they are composite lines drawn from different glands. The viscid spiral of the orb weaver snare is composed of a double groundline on which is superimposed a thin coating of viscid silk. Only when this line is spun in a particular way does it take on the characteristic form of a beaded necklace. Then the viscid spiral line is spun rather slowly and, as it is spun, the spider pulls out this elastic, coated line and lets it go with a jerk. As a result, the fluid is arranged in globules, spaced along the thread and far more sticky than a uniform covering.

Upon issuing from the spigots on the ends of the spinnerets the fluid hardens quickly to form the familiar silken thread. Spider silk is noted for its strength and elasticity. The tensile strength is said to be far stronger than steel. Some of the threads will stretch one-half their length before they break. The thinnest lines are only one-millionth of an inch wide and thus invisible to the human eye, but other lines are much heavier. Spiders produce enormous quantities of silk and use it in a number of ways.

### The Dragline

No better illustration of the depend-ince of all spiders on silk is afforded than the habit of laying down a drag-line or securing thread. Wherever the spider goes, it always plays out from the spinnerets a silken line that is attached at intervals to the substratum. It is analogous to the practice of playing out a rope when one enters the recesses of a deep cave or moves up and down the slope of a precipitous mountain. This dragline, which is actually com-posed of two or rarely, four intimately connected threads, is a constant com-panion of spiders of all kinds and all ages. At intervals the spider secures the line by pressing down the spinnerets pasting it to the surface by means of an attachment disk.

The dragline is useful as a lifeline to prevent falls from precipitous sur-faces, and it may serve as a means of escaping enemies. Spiders often drop or leap into the air and swing safely out of reach of a pursuer. A great many of the silken threads, or cobwebs, we see everywhere about us—on plants, on buildings, on the walls of our houses, where they often become unsightly, lint-covered streamers—are discarded drag-lines indicating that spiders have passed by. Long strands are floated in the air to form bridging lines from tree to tree or across streams, and on these are laid down the many types of aerial webs.

### Ballooning

On favorable days during the spring and especially during Indian summer, small spiders let out draglines from their spinnerts and are wafted through the air by the wind. This *ballooning*

*A young jumping spider sends out a double ballooning thread as it prepares to soar in the wind. Its dragline can be seen extending from its body to the toothpick on which it is standing*

is truly one of the strangest things that spiders do. Before taking off, the spiderlings are impelled to seek a promontory in their environment, a tall stalk of grass, a bush, a stone, or a fence rail. They face the direction of the wind, extend their legs to the fullest, and tilt their abdomens upward. The threads from the spinners are seized and drawn out by the air currents until long enough to maintain their weight, and then they let go. Tremendous distances have been covered by spiderlings on their silken filaments. Darwin recorded the arrival of ballooning spiders on the *Beagle* when 60 miles from land, and saw them sail away again after letting out new lines to catch the winds. They have dropped upon the rigging of ships when they were more than two hundred miles from the nearest land, but the average distance of flight is probably only a few hundred feet or yards. They have been intercepted as aerial plankton high in the air at 10,000 feet.

The dispersal of spiders throughout the world has been greatly facilitated by this strange habit. Ballooning is often interpreted as being a protective device. The scattering of the many young from the site of the egg sac seemingly eliminates the possibility of overcrowding and fratricide and improves the chances of survival of each tiny aeronaut. Not the sole province of the baby spider, ballooning is practiced by many adult spiders, the limitation to its accomplishment being mainly size and weight.

## Gossamer

Dragline silk largely makes up the drifting flakes known in prose and poetry as gossamer, a name of uncertain derivation but possibly from "goose summer" in "reference to the fanciful resemblance of the fragile skeins of silk from the down of geese, which the thrifty housewife causes to fly when she renovates her feather beds and pillows." The season is known in France as "fils de la Vierge," and in Germany as "Marienfaden" or Our Lady's threads. The reference here regards gossamer as being "the remnant of Our Lady's winding sheet which fell away in these lightest fragments as she was assumed into heaven." Great showers of gossamer have fallen in many places in the world, and their origin has been subject to many fantastic interpretations. The true explanation is a very simple one.

During the autumn months spiders become greatly active and cover the meadows and shrubbery with innumerable filaments which soon form a thin webbing over everything. Many are put out by spiders in unsuccessful attempts to fly, and are left hanging on the vegetation. The matted threads, or gossamer are picked up by the wind and showered down in spots often far from where the loose flocculent mass originated. Vast sheets are deposited almost every year in natural traps in the Yosemite Valley of California, and similar showers have been recorded from many parts of the world.

## Retreats, Nests, and Egg Sacs

A great many spiders hide in crevices or conceal themselves beneath debris, seemingly making little effort to establish a permanent place of refuge. Others have gone to great lengths to establish a residence that offers shelter from the sun and rain and a measure of protection from their enemies. Many line a space beneath a stone with silk and partially or completely enclose themselves in a silken cell. Some of our wolf spiders dig burrows into the earth and line the walls with silk. If suitable materials are at hand, the mouth of the burrow may be embellished with a turret made of sticks, leaves, or stones, cemented together with silk. Another refinement of great interest is the capping of the entrance with a hinged door made of sand and silk. A few of our wolf spiders build such trap-doors but this remarkable device is a constant

Female

BLACK WIDOW SPIDER

Male

WOLF SPIDER

TURRET SPIDER

CRAB SPIDER

GRASS SPIDER

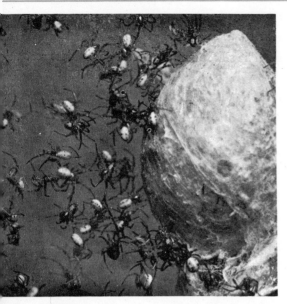

*Dozens of newly hatched black widow spiders emerge from their silken egg case*

feature on the burrows of the trap-door spiders of our South and Southwest. The cork door of some of these spiders is a plug that, fitting the beveled edges of the burrow much as a cork in a bottle, is further held down securely by the powerful spider. The folding-door tarantulas get their name from the fact that their burrow is closed by two flaps that meet on the midline. The purse-web tarantulas continue the silk of the burrow up the side of a tree as a long tube. Whenever an insect crawls over the surface of the tube, which soon becomes covered with lichens and debris, the waiting spider rushes to that point and expertly transfixes the prey by biting through the silken lining. Once captured, the prey is hauled into the tube through an incision, that is later repaired.

The retreats of spiders that live on vegetation are extremely varied in appearance and workmanship. Providing an adequate roof may involve the tremendous task of bending or folding one or more leaves, spikes, or stalks of grass in such a way that a more or

less spacious, waterproof retreat is afforded for the spider and the eggs. The retreat can hardly be considered apart from the egg sac inasmuch as the latter is usually the central theme and often the incentive for producing the domicile. It often represents the last effort of the mother spider in behalf of a new generation she will never see. In its simplest form the egg sac is only a few threads that hold the mass together.

The long-legged cellar spider, *Pholcus phalangioides,* carries the lightly tied mass in her jaws. In many spiders the cover is relatively superficial and the eggs can be seen through the thin webbing. However, in many species the sacs are durably made objects, hardened and toughened by various means, covered over with sand or debris, and sometimes tinted in pleasing yellows, reds, and blues. The wolf spiders spin a sheet, deposit the eggs, cover them with a second sheet, and then mold the whole into a more or less spherical body, that is carried attached to the spinnerets. Many comb-footed spiders leave their round sacs suspended in their webs at the center of a maze of threads. The argiopes spin three separate layers of padding around their eggs. Some other spiders hide them away, camouflage them, or even suspend them in the air on the ends of threads. In general, spiders show little maternal solicitude for their eggs or young, but notable exceptions are the wolf and fisher spiders which carry the eggs around with them or spin complicated nursery webs for the family.

### The Snare

The silk-spinning activities of spiders reach their highest expression in the production of the many types of webs, or snares. The intricate patterns of some and the symmetrical beauty of others often incite admiration. Few people realize that spiders are almost the only animals that make traps to capture their food. Except for man and a few other animals, such as the caddisflies and fungus gnats, the practice of making a snare is peculiar to spiders. The realization of the many strange devices is a triumph of instinctive behavior since spiders are guided only by instinct and have nothing of the power called intelligence.

As is to be expected, the hunting spiders that run in upright posture produce few webs of note. The grass spiders, which have become sedentary secondarily, spread out an expansive sheet of webbing over the soil or vegetation and spin above it a tangled superstructure of threads. Flying and jumping insects are halted in midair and drop to the yielding surface of the sheet over which they walk with great difficulty, whereas the agile spider can run rapidly to capture them before they can reach the edge.

The aerial spiders lift their snares off the ground and fill, often with networks of threads, a considerable amount of space. The comb-footed spiders spin a maze of threads and anchor it to the substratum with long guy lines on the ends of which are globules of viscid silk. Walking insects get caught on the viscid lines, are covered with silk combed out by the hind legs of the spider, and then are lifted by block and tackle methods to the labyrinth. The sheet web weavers spin a sheet at the center of the maze and run over the lower surface. Flying insects strike the net of threads and drop through to the sheet surface, where the spider grasps them and pulls them through the sheet webbing. The orb web would seem to stand alone as a glorious creation, an incredible novelty designed by superior artisans. Actually, it is only the end product in a series of steps that began at the center of the tangle of threads grouped around the precious egg sac. It is a superb space web that, surpassing all other types in beauty, design, and efficiency, brings to the thickset aerialist

a choice assortment of flying insects.

## Commercial Use of Spider Silk

With spider silk so abundant, it would seem that it should be valuable as a commercial product. As long ago as 1709, a Frenchman, Bon de Saint-Hilaire, of Montepelier, France, demonstrated that it was usuable for fabrics in the same way as the silk of the silkworm. However, the practical difficulties of rearing large numbers of spiders, of feeding them living insect food, and of keeping them segregated to prevent cannibalism are so great that it is doubtful that spider silk will ever become of commercial importance. The use of spider lines as reticules in various optical instruments is a direct consequence of the fineness of the fibers and of their great strength and ability to withstand extremes of weather conditions. The place of spider silk, however, is now largely being supplanted by platinum filaments and by engraving on glass plates. For bombsights, range finders, periscopes, and most gunsights, the width of the line has to be carefully adapted to the optical purposes and characteristics of the instrument. Etched glass is obviously necessary in most such instances, as it would be impossible to accomplish the desired result with spider silk. —W.J.G.

*Recommended Reading*

**American Spiders**—W. J. Gertsch. D. Van Nostrand Company, Inc., New York.
**The Biology of Spiders**—T.H. Savory. Sidgwick and Jackson, London.
**The Common Spiders of the United States**—James H. Emerton. Dover Publications, New York.
**How to Know the Spiders**—B.J. and Elizabeth Kaston. William C. Brown Company, Dubuque, Iowa.
**The Life of The Spider**—John Crompton. Houghton Mifflin Company, Boston.
**The Spider Book**—John H. Comstock. Doubleday, Doran, New York.
**The Spider's Web**—T.H. Savory. Frederick Warne & Company, London and New York.
**The Story of Spiders**—Dorothy Shuttlesworth. Garden City Books, Garden City, New York.

In cross-section, the underground tunnel of a trap-door spider reveals an intricate silk-lined construction 8 to 12 inches deep

## The Trap-door Spider

Like styles for women, popular interest in certain forms of wildlife sometimes comes to the fore, then wanes. At least it seems so with the trap-door spider. Before the turn of the century, magazines featured it, and travelers knew well the unique dwelling that it builds.

In 1884 Richard A. Proctor in discussing the spider fauna of southern California said: "Among the most valued trophies tourists carry away with them from the coast are neat cards adorned with these animals and a case containing the nest so arranged as to show its wonderful trapdoor and the delicate lining of the interior."

About this time, two travel writers, Alex J. Sweet and J. Armory Knox, pictured its abode as "lined with some material as soft and glossy as white satin. At the surface of the ground is a small opening, into which fits a door made of sand and gravel glued together with some gummy fluid, and lined with the same satin material as the nest. The door opens and shuts on hinges made of many strands of a silken sort of thread." Then they went on to explain that when it "goes out into the world," it pockets the "key to its night latch," so that, "the sharpest eye could not detect the nest or its entrance, for the outside of the door is formed of sand and gravel that looks exactly like the surrounding soil."

T.S. Van Dyke in 1886 described how in southern California the trap-door spider builds its nest in the ground "lined with soft, white stuff of silky appearance and covered by a trapdoor with a perfect hinge."

The most novel account revolved around a Mr. Treadwell who, collecting in California for the British Museum, found a nest and managed to dig it up complete with occupant. He put it in a tin box with a lid and journeyed overland to San Francisco, 350 miles to the north of his hunting grounds. From there, with his captive, he sailed for London. Arriving, he examined the box and noted the creature to be very much alive. He registered at a hotel in the Strand and that evening had his meal, leaving the container in his room. While he was away, a chambermaid entered and, curious, took the lid off the box.

The spider rushed out. She screamed and flung the box against the wall, with the unhappy results that the adobe nest crumbled.

In 1756 Patrick Browne in his *Civil and Natural History of Jamaica* first described the trapdoor, illustrating the nest of a West Indian species. A few years later, the Abbe Sauvages likened nests of certain spiders near Montpellier, France, to "little rabbit burrows lined with silk and closed with a tightly fitting movable door." Although these burrows capped with their trapdoor continued to attract popular admiration, no careful comprehensive study was made of them until 1873, when J. T. Moggridge published his *Harvesting Ants and Trap-Door Spiders.*

In southern California lives *Bothriocyrtum californicum*, which excavates a simple, 8- to 12-inch-deep tube with a web-hinged door of as many as 30 alternate layers of silk and earth. Bevel-edged like a cork, which explains its name, "cork" door, it fits snugly into an opening about the size of a silver half-dollar. The underside of the door, as well as the inside of the hole, is coated with web, but sticks and earth camouflage the outside of the lid so that it appears like its surroundings. In searching for these nests in adobe land around San Diego and hills bounding the northern part of Los Angeles, one may be forced to get down on his hand and knees before he can see the three-quarter circle outline—the door.

Other than the "cork" door, some species manufacture the so-called "wafer" door. It, too, works up and down on a broad, silk hinge, but instead of being bevel-edged, it possesses an outside circular flange that over-hangs the entrance to the burrow. It may be slightly concave so that it fits better into it. Some burrows have a thin outer door and a second door partway down; others are closed on the outside by a thin door, with a slanting side tunnel that joins the main tube, its opening having a trapdoor; and still others are even more complicated.

In determing how the trap-door spider can dig its burrow, we know that it owns a comblike rake of large spines on the margins of its chelicerae, which constitutes its digging tool. Aided by this, it cuts and scrapes away minute particles of earth, molding them into balls and transporting them outside of the hole. Deeper and deeper it hews this subterranean shelter, until the desired depth has been attained.

In fashioning the door to its nest, it brings damp soil from the bottom and dabs it on the side of the entrance, packing it down solidly with its mandibles. Turning around, with its spinnerets it weaves a trail of web. First comes the fresh earth, then the silk, until the cover reaches about a third across the opening. Then it raises the partly finished door and folds it

*The top of the trap-door spider's tunnel has a hinged door that is opened and closed by its occupant*

back to a vertical position, with the webbed part still attached forming the hinge. With the door this way, it continues the process until it is completed. To waterproof the walls of the burrow, it coats them with saliva and earth, making the surface smooth and firm, after which it applies a silken lining. This lining varies in thickness and may, or may not, cover the whole tunnel.

As the spider grows, it enlarges its abode in the same manner. At times rocks in the soil force it to curve the tube out and in, or, if there are too many barriers, it will dig its quarters in a more suitable location. Although it sticks to its hearth, one will learn that should he take some spiders and insert them in a tub of earth in his backyard laboratory, they will shortly excavate typical retreats. In fact, if removed from its premises and deposited in an unoccupied tunnel, or a cavity

scooped out for it, it quickly remodels this to conform with the pattern of its original home.

A single, mature trap-door spider resides in a single dwelling. After mating, the female in the bottom of her lair deposits from 200 to 300 eggs and weaves a cocoon about them. With their hatching, pearl-colored spiderlings, each the size of a grain of rice, emerge. With their growth and moltings, they change color—to pink, then darker, and finally the black hue of the adult. Upon leaving the nest, they build pencil-size burrows of their own.

When detecting the tread of a sow bug or other nocturnal insect close to its den, the trap-door spider crawls to the top and thrusts its body part way out, grabs the prey and at its leisure sucks out its life juices. Should it venture outside of its dugout, it finds it difficult to reenter, for the door fastens so tightly in the tube that only

*A female trap-door spider emerges from her tunnel to close its hinged door*

a fine crack remains where a claw could be inserted to lift it.

While it is hunting for food, it must be on guard against the *Pepsis* wasp. When this insect alights near the door, the spider may interpret it as potential prey, and push its door slightly open. The wasp, seizing its opportunity, flies into the burrow and stings and paralyzes the spider. Then it drags the spider to the bottom of the burrow and lays an egg on it. When the wasp grub hatches, it feeds upon the body of the spider.

When the trapdoor is closed, no insect can invade the trap-door spider's chamber. Should the vibrations from a form of life walking above it not be to its liking, it hastens up and hooks its fangs into the underside of the door, bracing itself. Upon such occasions one may stick the point of a penknife into the door crack, and pry and bend it almost to the breaking point before the cover gives. One investigator asserts that the trap-door spider is capable of resisting a lift on its door estimated at 10 pounds or more.

That naturalists are really missing something by neglecting our trap-door spider can be seen by this comment from Willis J. Gertsch, Curator of Spiders at the American Museum of Natural History, New York City: "Many spiders tunnel into the soil, but the true trap-door spiders of the family Ctenizidae are the most accomplished burrowers and the most gifted artisans. They and their relatives can claim to be the inventors of that superb mechanism to insure privacy, the trapdoor, for they represent a stock that was probably capping burrows with doors long before many true spider emulators were evolved." —W.D.W.

**SPHAGNUM** (*See under Bog*)

**SPITTLEBUG** (*See under Froghopper and Treehopper*)

# SPONGE

Although they resemble plants in their immobility, and often in their growth habits, sponges are animals. They are of simple, even primitive, organization, but they are abundant in all oceans, and one family even inhabits fresh water.

The internal structure of all sponges (phylum Porifera) is basically the same. An outer layer of cells forms the protective covering. A middle layer may be one cell wide and nonsupportive, or it may be greatly thickened and contain deposits of calcium carbonate or of spongin that form a supporting skeleton. The third, internal layer is made up of digestive cells, each equipped with a whiplike filament, or flagellum.

These three layers of tissue are arranged in a typically vaselike form, surrounding a mass of water. Numerous holes connect the water on the outside with the water on the inside. The flagellae set up currents that bring the minute animal life and plantlife on which the sponges feed, into the central chamber and that exhaust waste matter through the large hole at the top.

In the simplest, most primitive sponges, all of the digestive cells are located on the interior of the animal, around the inside of the "vase." In the next, more highly developed type, short canals emptying into the interior are covered with the digestive cells, while the interior itself is lined with the same tough cells that are present in the outer covering. In the highest type of sponge, including all of the ones that have skeletons of fiber, the canal system within the middle layer of tissue is complex, and the digestive cells are scattered along these canals.

Sponges are extremely variable in shape. Some are nearly spherical, others shaped like open baskets, some are branching, others are compact. A considerable variety exists within the same species, as water pressure at different

*Sponges inhabit all oceans and one group lives in fresh water. Their form, even within species, varies greatly with such external factors as depth and living space*

depths and the availability of space for expansion affects the individual shape.

The skeleton of the simpler sponges of the first two types are of calcium carbonate and are hard and brittle. Most of the more highly evolved species in the thrid type have skeletons made of *spongin*—a chemical with a composition similar to that of silk. The fibers are interlaced, giving strength and flexibility to the tissues. It is this dried and cleaned skeleton that forms the sponge of commerce.

In some of the sponges of the third type, spongin is not present, and the skeleton is made up of minute needle-shaped particles of carbonate or of silicon. These are called spicules, and they have many forms, each characteristic of the species that produced it.

Sponges have two different methods of reproduction—by division and by sexual reproduction. A section of the wall, containing the three layers of tissue, may expand, then pinch off and drop to the bottom to develop as a small imitation of the parent. Sexual reproduction in sponges involves the mating of sex cells of both kinds produced by the same parent. The larvae develop within the parent into a free-swimming stage and then pass out through the hole (osculum) at the top. After undergoing further development, the larvae sink to the bottom, attach themselves to it, and become stationary. —G.B.S.

*Recommended Reading*

**Field Book of Seashore Life**—Roy Waldo Miner. G.P. Putnam's Sons, New York.

# SPOONBILL
**Roseate Spoonbill**
**Other Common Names** — Pink curlew
**Scientific Name** — *Ajaia ajaja*
**Family** — Threskiornithidae (ibises and spoonbills)
**Order** — Ciciniiformes
**Size** — Length, 32 inches
**Range** — From Florida Bay and the Texas coast south through the Bahamas, both coasts of Mexico, the West Indies, and South America to Argentina

Spoonbills are heronlike waterbirds closely related to ibises (*See Ibis*). Of the 28 species of ibises and spoonbills that occur in most of the tropical regions of the world, five of these are spoonbills. Four species of spoonbills live in the Old World and are largely white, whereas the roseate spoonbill, the only one in the western hemisphere, is distinctly rose-colored with carmine wing coverts.                     — J.K.T.

## The Roseate Spoonbill
The roseate spoonbill is one of the rarer birds of this country. In many ways and indeed, in general appearance, it seems a relic of forgotten ages, a lingering living echo of the Age of Reptiles, for there is no other bird like it. Few large species are so brilliantly plumaged, none of them has so odd an appearance.

There was a time not many years ago when they occurred in much greater numbers than they do today but spoonbills never attained the abundance of such companion species as the ibises and herons. Largely confined to the southern Atlantic area and Gulf Coast regions, they suffered the penalty of possessing beautiful plumage and, like the egrets, were singled out by fashion for various decorative purpose (*See account under Egret and under Heron*). The plume hunter followed the birds into their remotest mangrove haunts

*The roseate spoonbill is a rare bird, now mainly confined to swamplands along the Atlantic and Gulf coasts*

and hundreds of them were slain for the manufacture of feather fans, hat trimmings and fish lures. "Civilization" such as that and spoonbills do not mix!

Associating with other colonial nesting birds like the herons and ibises, it bred in several of the time-honored "rookeries" of Florida but even when it enjoyed a comparatively common status, its movements and nesting were erratic and unpredictable. It seems very strange that so conspicuous and desirable a species from the student ornithologist's point of view remained for so long somewhat of a mystery. Nobody was quite sure of what its food was, when it reached nesting age, or why it frequented one area in spring and summer and another quite close by in fall and winter. It remained for the National Audubon Society, ever the champion of persecuted birds, to do something about this lack of knowledge of this species.

Although for many years the spoonbill was a special charge of Audubon Society sanctuary wardens, where it happened to occur, it was not until the fall of 1939 that the first detailed field study of the bird was undertaken. The result of the subsequent two years of work by Robert P. Allen, then Director of the National Audubon Society Sanctuaries, was embodied in his Research Report No. 2 of the National Audubon Society, and constitutes practically everything that was known up to the time about this highly interesting species.

There are only two states where one can be sure of seeing spoonbills today, and then only in very restricted areas and at the right time of year. Amid the mangrove-studded Florida Keys one nesting colony still persists in winter. In summer along the tidal rivers that flow from the Everglades into the maze of the Ten Thousand Islands, scattered bands of spoonbills range from Tampa Bay down to Cape Sable. The other locality constitutes a few of the low-lying, thickly grown islands of the Texas

*Roseate spoonbills*

When choosing a mate, the female roseate spoonbill first repulses the advances of the male (1); then accepts a stick from him with which she starts the nest (2). The male vigorously defends his mate against other adult males (3); and when the nest is essentially complete, the birds mate (4)

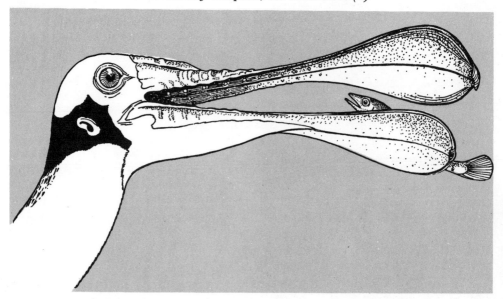

The upper mandible of the roseate spoonbill's bill may be six inches long and two inches across at its broad tip. A Lateral groove running the length of the upper mandible and ending in a "Nail" probably is the main sensory system of the bill and aids the bird in feeding, as do the Papillae, or dental-like processes, on both the upper and lower mandibles. Food is transferred to the throat or to the Gular pouch by slightly shaking the head

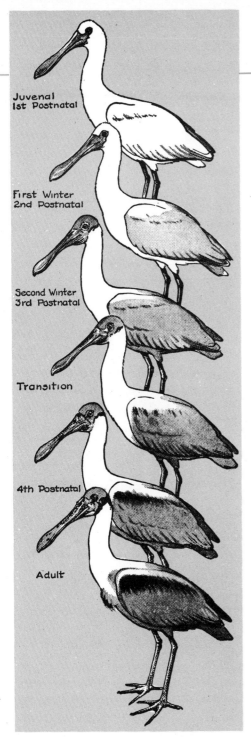

The roseate spoonbill changes from white juvenal plumage (1), through a partial molt (2), and three complete molts (3, 4, 6), to attain its deep pink and white adult plumage. The molting period takes three years and the birds are not ready to breed until the adult plumage is acquired

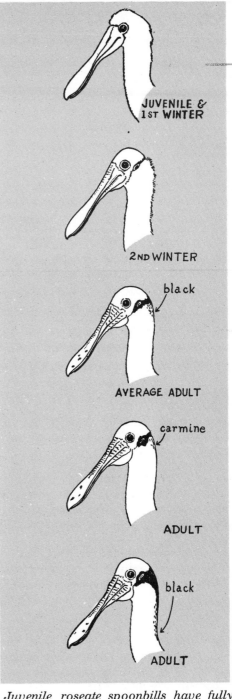

Juvenile roseate spoonbills have fully feathered heads until the time of the first complete molt (between 15 and 25 months). Adults have bare, apple-green to golden-buff colored heads and black skin around the ear opening and on the nape of the neck. Some individuals have carmine feather tufts on the back of their necks and the bare black area may vary in extent

coast from the southern portion of Galveston Bay practically to Brownsville.

It is in Texas that most of the promise for the spoonbills' future lies. The colonies there have done well under Audubon warden protection and have been on the steady increase with very satisfactory "crops" of young raised annually. The Florida birds still have been unaccountably declining and the work of fact-finding in connection with yet unanswered questions regarding their movements is by no means over.

The two outstanding characteristics of the spoonbill are its plumage color and the remarkable spoon-shaped bill. For the first three years of its life the bird is white; the rosy shade and carmine shoulders are marks of adulthood. It is not until this age is reached that the birds pair and nest. Highly temperamental in domestic habits, the spoonbill will quickly desert a site if disturbed while nest-building or egg-laying is going on.

One can never forget the first observance of these birds, or indeed any subsequent sight of them, for they are always an unusual experience in field study. Glowing with unbelievable color against the cobalt background of a Gulf sky, or framed amid the intense greenery of mangroves, huisache, or ebony, the spoonbill etches itself upon one's memory in an unforgettable picture of almost fantastic beauty. No bird known to many experienced observers produces quite the same effect as it does; no bird, except perhaps the anhinga, brings so vividly to mind the impression that it belongs to another age (*See Anhinga*). To see a flock standing rigidly immobile atop a mangrove bush or upon a submerged sandbar, all facing in the same direction with their outlandish bills resting against their breasts and the living color all but pulsing in the sunlight, is like looking backward through the ages to the time of the prehistoric dinosaurs.                —A.S.,Jr.

*Recommended Reading*

The Roseate Spoonbill—Robert Porter Allen. Research Report No. 2, The National Audubon Society, New York.

*Spring beauty*

## SPRING BEAUTY
**Other Common Names**—Claytonia
**Scientific Name**—*Claytonia virginica*
**Family**—Portulacaceae (purslane family)
**Range**—Southwestern Quebec and western and southern New England to southern Ontario and Minnesota, south to Georgia, Alabama, Mississippi, Louisiana, and Texas
**Habitat**—Rich woods, thickets, and clearings
**Time of Blooming**—March through May

This dainty pink flower with its deeper pink veins is one of the harbingers of spring. The slender leaves are thick and the several 5-petaled flowers are grouped at the top of a 6- to 12-inch stem. The flowers open only while the light is strong and close quickly when picked. Only day-flying insects visit them. Each petal is marked with a pink line ending in a yellow blotch at its base. This serves as a nectar guide for the bumblebees and the little brown bee flies, among other insect visitors. Self-fertilization is prevented by the stigmatic surfaces remaining pressed together until the pollen from the anthers have been dispersed.

The plant stores food for early growth and flowering in a deeply buried bulb. These bulbs were one of the favorite spring foods of the Indians, but today the plant has become less common and should not be gathered for that purpose. In many states it is protected by being on wildflower conservation lists.

The spring beauty is a member of the purslane family. One would scarcely suspect that the *pussley* of the gardens is a near relative, but it is a member of the same family.

There are about 10 species of spring beauty native to North America. The Carolina spring beauty has white flowers and seldom grows any place except in the mountains. One species, in the western states, resembles the eastern spring beauty while another, *Claytonia sibirica*, has become a naturalized citizen from Europe.

In the northwestern United States the bulb of a species of spring beauty provides considerable food for the western pocket gopher. In the East the white-footed mouse, which feeds on the seeds, fruits, and roots or tubers of a variety of these plants, includes spring beauty in its diet to a limited extent (*See Wildflower*).

## SPRING PEEPER (*See under Tree Frog*)

## SPRUCE

The spruces are a large and successful group of evergreens that grow in both the eastern and western hemispheres. Almost without exception they are most successful in cool, rather moist climates, often in mountainous country, and several of them occur in subarctic regions. North America has seven native species plus the introduced Norway spruce. Black spruce, *Picia mariana*, shares with the white spruce, *P. glauca*, a range that stretches across Canada from Alaska to the New England and North Central States, and forms lush stands in swampy areas. It has very short needles that give the overall foliage a rather fine-grained appearance and very small cones hardly more than an inch long. Those of the white spruce are about twice this length, narrower in proportion, and the needles which sometimes have a pale, whitish bloom on them, are also longer than those of the black spruce. White spruce occurs farther westward in the United States, into the Rocky Mountain region, and grows to a larger average size with a maximum height of about 140 feet. Black spruce has a maximum height of about 100 feet but sometimes grows

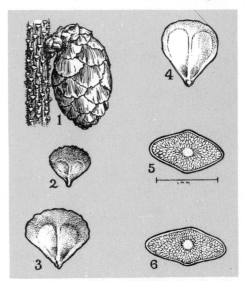

*The appearance of spruce cones (1) varies with species; since, the cone scales (2, 3, 4) are distinct for each tree; as are the cross-sections of needles (5, 6). The cone scales shown are from black, red, and white spruce in that order*

no larger than a shrub and is a very slow growing species. Its wood stands exposure to water well and is used for such purposes as canoe paddles, ladders, shipbuilding and for paper pulp.

Red spruce, *Picea rubens,* is a common eastern tree in the New England and Appalachian areas and does not naturally occur west of Ohio. Its yellow-green needles and reddish-brown cones are typical sights in the upland areas in which it grows. Colorado spruce, *Picea abies,* as typical of western mountains as the red spruce is of the East, has an entirely different coloration and considerably larger cones than either of the previously mentioned species. Its attractively colored foliage is thick and neat looking on younger trees and with adaquate water it does well almost anywhere except perhaps in very heavy clay soils, which makes it a favorite among nurserymen.

Among the other American spruces most grow in the western states and several species are of impressive size, attractive appearance, and considerable importance in the lumber industry. Outstanding among these is the Englemann spruce, *P. engelmannii,* of the Rocky Mountains. Although this tree seldom grows to much over a 100 feet in height, 64 million board feet of it were cut during one year in the 1940's. Of equal or greater importance for lumber is the Sitka spruce, *P. sitchensis,* which grows along the Pacific coastal border from northern California to Alaska. This giant tree may grow to nearly 300 feet in height with a trunk yards in diameter, and it has a very characteristic shape to its branches. On lower portions of the tree these may sweep the ground but turn upward at the tips and have branchlets that hang in a tassel-like fringe along most of their length. As their geographical range would indicate, Sitka spruces need a great deal of

*Red spruce trees dot the higher slopes of Great Smokies National Park, Tennessee*

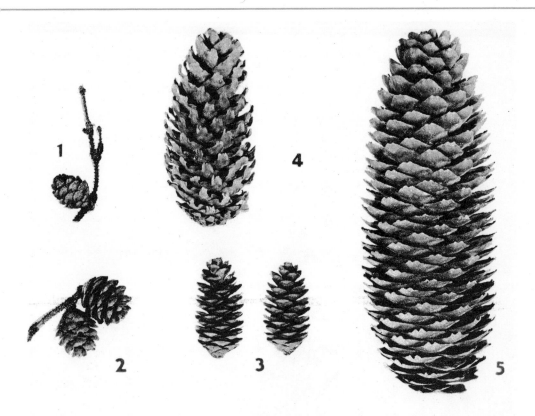

*Spruce cones, (1) black spruce, (2) red spruce; (3) white spruce; (4) blue spruce;*
*(5) Norway spruce*

moisture and a rather cool climate. In the most favorable combination of these conditions the massive trunks are buttressed and supported in the soft ground by great surface roots, but in the severe climate of the extreme north and higher altitudes Sitka spruce may be reduced in size to hardly more than a shrub. This is also true of many trees that range into the arctic areas or to timberline elevations.

Weeping spruce, *Picia breweriana*, a species of very limited range on the California-Oregon border not too far inland from the sea, has a tassle-like quality to its foliage even more pronounced than the Sitka spruce, but, like it, has needles that are rather flattened and triangular in cross-section, rather than square as in the other spruce

species. It is a relatively small tree for the West, usually less than 100 feet in height.                           —M.H.B.

### Identifying Spruces

Just as it is easy to recognize a pine by the way its needles are borne in little bundles, or fascicles (*see under Pine*), it is a simple matter to tell a spruce, that is, to distinguish it from a pine, fir, hemlock, or larch.

The spruce characters that are most important to know are two. First, the leaf is borne, not in bundles, as in the pines, but singly, at the tip of a tiny knob or peg, so that when the leaves fall off (they stay on the twig sometimes for 10 years) these myriads of tiny, peglike projections are left, making the twigs decidedly rough to the

*Blue spruce (left), white spruce (right)*

touch. This applies especially, of course, to the old twigs where the leaves have fallen. Many of these twigs, usually dead, will be found around the base of the trunk, or in the interior branch system, where they have been cut off from the light. Although there are other members of the pine family whose twigs are roughened by old leaf bases, there is none that has this character so markedly as the genus *Picea,* the spruces.

Second, the leaf of the spruce may more aptly be called a needle than the leaf of any other of our eastern conifers. Fir and hemlock needles, for example, are flat; and although such things as flattened needles, for special purposes, are used in the arts, it is quite likely that the ordinary person thinks of a needle as a rather long, narrow, cylindrical object with a sharp point at one end. The needles of the spruces are not really cylindrical, although they appear so to the casual observer. A spruce needle is really four-sided, but in our eastern spruces the sides are so narrow that they are scarcely visible to the naked eye. But they can readily be seen with a hand lens, and a cross cut through a leaf brings out its true shape.

There is a group of western and Oriental spruces that have more or less flattened leaves, but these are comparatively few, and they are rarely seen in the East. Even in these trees, the leaves, though flattened, are really four-sided.

The cones of the spruces resemble those of the pines, firs, and hemlocks, but they do not stand up on the branches as do those of the cedar (*Cedrus*) and the firs; they are pendent and usually occur only in the upper part of the tree. Their characters are important in distinguishing the various kinds of spruces.           —A.H.G.

## Colorado Spruce

**Other Common Names** — Blue spruce, silver spruce

**Scientific Name** — *Picea pungens*
**Family** — Pinaceae (pine family)
**Range** — Rocky Mountains, from Montana southward nearly to Mexico. Particularly abundant in Wyoming, Colorado, and Utah
**Habitat** — Naturally a tree of intermediate altitudes in the West, but a common ornamental (cultivated) tree elsewhere
**Leaves** — Firm, forward-curving needles up to 1¼ inches long, with sharp points and with the powder-blue color most noticeable on new foliage at the ends of branches
**Bark** — Brown-gray with a flaky, almost prickly surface
**Flowers** — Male: drooping and yellow-red. Female: upright, conelike flowers and of a purplish and green color
**Fruit** — Hanging cones, 2¼ to 4 inches long, the long scales with thin and often wavy, turned down edges

The Colorado spruce, *Picea pungens,* of Colorado, New Mexico, Utah, and Wyoming, and thus of rather limited distribution in the Rocky Mountains region, was introduced into cultivation in 1862. With each passing year it is being more widely planted, and it is well adapted to dry climates, or to regions where droughts are apt to occur. Individuals vary greatly in the blueness of their leaves. The Koster spruce, var. *kosteriana,* is an especially blue variety which can be propagated by grafting. The blue spruce, often called the Colorado blue spruce, or just Colorado spruce, is certainly one of our most striking conifers, if not our most handsome; and individual specimens, of symmetrical, cone-shaped form, are appraised at many hundreds of dollars simply for their ornamental value.

—A.H.G.

## Norway Spruce

**Other Common Names** — European spruce
**Scientific Name** — *Picea abies*
**Family** — Pinaceae (pine family)
**Range** — Central and northern Europe.

Commonly planted in North America except in dry areas

**Habitat**—Coniferous forests

**Leaves**—Bluntly pointed green needles, ½ to 1 inch long, each one growing, as do all spruce needles, from a tiny butt or spur on the twig. Twigs hang like tassels

**Bark**—Mixed gray, brown, and reddish tones, and flaky on the young trunks; duller and smoother later on. Often stained with greenish resin

**Flower**—Tiny (male) catkins and (female) conelike forms borne on the tips of the branches in spring

**Fruit**—Large, four- to seven-inch, cigar-shaped cones becoming thicker and sharp-edged as they dry and open to release the winged seeds

The Norway spruce, *Picea abies*, a native of northern Europe and Asia, is by far the commonest cultivated species. In fact, if we except the Colorado spruce, this is the principal spruce planted in parks, cemeteries, and private grounds. It is a beautiful ornamental tree, of symmetrical form, but it has withal a certain somber aspect, perhaps due to the very dark green foliage densely covering its hosts of drooping branches and branchlets. Having been long in cultivation, more than 50 varieties are distinguished, based for the most part either on the character and color of the needles, or on the form of the tree.

It grows rapidly in youth, but after the age of forty years or more, except in favored locations, it usually begins to decline in beauty as well as in general well-being, the top becoming thin and ragged. It is possible that, like the native spruces, the balsam fir, and the red pine, it is intolerant of excessive summer heat and perhaps also the extreme variability of North America's winter weather; for in its native home, the temperature extremes are not so great, or at least the changes are not so rapid. The cones of Norway spruces are large—up to 6 or 7 inches in length, and from 1½ to 2 inches in diameter, being larger than the cones of native North American spruces. The cone scales are truncate, that is, appearing as if cut off at the ends; or sometimes only notched or toothed. Further, the twigs are glabrous, so that this species cannot be confused with the black and red spruces; nor do the leaves have, at least in the typical form, the whitish coloration of the white spruce.

The wood of the Norway spruce is known in England as *white deal*. Being finely grained and of a homogeneous texture so that it readily transmits sound vibrations, it is admirably adapted to the manufacture of violins, pianos, and other musical instruments. Throughout northern Europe it serves as the Christmas tree, well known to us in the tales of Hans Christian Andersen. But with us it is not so satisfactory for this purpose as the balsam fir, because the needles fall off more quickly than in the latter species, and the odor is not so pleasantly resinous.

In Europe the bark of the Norway spruce is sometimes used for tanning leather; in many Scandinavian countries the young shoots furnish winter fodder for cattle and sheep; baskets are made from the inner bark, and strong cords are twisted from the long and flexible roots, which are first split and boiled.

—A.H.G.

## White spruce

**Other Common Names**—Canadian spruce

**Scientific Name**—*Picea glauca*

**Family**—Pinaceae (pine family)

**Range**—Labrador to Alaska, south to Montana and New York

**Habitat**—Coniferous forest belt

**Leaves**—Quadrangular, one half to three quarters of an inch long, bluish-green

**Bark**—Grayish with flaky texture

**Flower**—Small pine catkin

**Fruit**—Cones, 1½ to 2 inches long, pale brown in color with smooth margins

The white spruce, *Picea glauca*, although one of our eastern native

*Norway spruce, a native of Europe, is widely cultivated in North America*

spruces, is really a northern spruce, growing naturally from Larbrador to Alaska, south to Montana, Minnesota, northern Wisconsin, Michigan, northern New York, and New England. It is occasionally cultivated, and one sometimes sees handsome planted specimens in southern New England; it is at home in Maine, where, along the rocky, irregular coastline, and on many of the islands that dot the coastal waters, it stands "with serried ranks within reach of the salty spray." With its near relatives, the red and black spruces, it forms a large part of the coniferous Canadian forest. —A.H.G.

*The gliding membrane, running from wrist to ankle along the sides of the southern flying squirrel's body, allow it to make downward glides of up to 125 feet*

**SQUIRREL**
**Southern Flying Squirrel**
**Other Common Names**—Flying squirrel, gliding squirrel
**Scientific Name**—*Glaucomys volans*
**Family**—Sciuridae (marmots, squirrels, and chipmunks)
**Order**—Rodentia
**Size**—Body length, 8½ to 10¼ inches; tail, 3½ to 4½ inches; weight, 1¾ to 4 ounces
**Range**—Eastern United States, except for northern New England and the northern Great Lakes area; west to eastern South Dakota and central Texas. Also in isolated areas of northwestern, central, and southern Mexico, and in Central America

At first sight the flying squirrel does not appear noticeably different from other squirrels, but when it leaps into space, the parachutelike membrane connecting its feet converts it into a tiny living glider. Twisting and banking with the aid of its featherlike tail, it can sail at a downward angle as far as 125 feet. The flight ends as it flips to an upright position on the trunk of another tree to climb again for the next leap and glide. Forests of beech and maple are its favorite habitat. It eats nuts, berries, seeds, birds, and insects. This little squirrel is active only at night, so even when abundant it is rarely seen. During the day it sleeps in an abandoned woodpecker hole, an unused gray squirrel nest, or even a birdhouse. In the winter many flying squirrels may hole up together, but during the spring and summer usually a mother and her two to six young are the only occupants of one nest. Owls and cats destroy many of these squirrels, but as long as their woodland or forest shelter remains, their population seems to hold its own.

**Fox Squirrel**
**Other Common Names**—Eastern fox squirrel
**Scientific Name**—*Sciurus niger*
**Family**—Sciuridae (marmots, squirrels, and chipmunks)
**Order**—Rodentia
**Size**—Body length, 19 to 28 inches; tail, 10 to 12¼ inches; weight, 1½ to 3 pounds
**Range**—Eastern United States north to southern Pennsylvania, the Great Lakes, and northern Minnesota and North Dakota, west through North Dakota to eastern Montana border, eastern South Dakota, extreme southeastern corner of Wyoming, northeastern Colorado, western Kansas, and Oklahoma, central Texas, and extreme northeastern Mexico

Our biggest and showiest squirrels, the fox squirrels, are the hardest to describe. From Pennsylvania to Maryland they may be steel-gray in color, but elsewhere their coats have a rusty tinge. In the South some have black-and-white faces and grizzled reddish fur, while others are entirely black with white noses and ears. Fox squirrels prefer open groves of hickory or oak, or the sunlit borders of cypress swamps, and avoid dense forests. For a home they may use hollow trees, or construct outdoor nests of twigs, leaves, and bark. In summer these nests may be flimsy affairs, but the tightly matted roof and sides of a winter nest keep its occupant warm and dry. Buried nuts and seeds are winter food, while in summer, buds, fruits, and some insects supplement this diet. In March or April two to four young are born, the mother squirrel raising the brood by herself.

Fat and relatively slow, fox squirrels make tasty meals for bobcats, foxes, and man. Hunting has almost exterminated these colorful squirrels in parts of their range and efforts should be made to save those remaining.

*The fox squirrel is a large, slow-moving mammal that has been nearly exterminated in some parts of its range*

### Gray Squirrel

**Other Common Names**—Eastern gray squirrel
**Scientific Name**—*Sciurus carolinensis*
**Family**—Sciuridae (marmots, squirrels, and chipmunks)
**Order**—Rodentia
**Size**—Body length, 15½ to 21 inches; tail, 7½ to 10 inches; weight, 1 to 1½ pounds
**Range**—Eastern United States, north to southern Canada, west to southern Manitoba, central North Dakota, Minnesota, Iowa, southeastern corner of Nebraska, eastern Kansas, eastern Oklahoma, and Texas

When settlers first began clearing the great eastern forests, hordes of squirrels sometimes destroyed entire corn crops. Less bountiful today, these squirrels are still abundant wherever there are plenty of oaks and hickories. In both woods and city parks the gray squirrel has become one of our most familiar mammals. Like most of its kind it is active by day, and particularly so in the fall as it busily caches its winter food supply. In the summer it feeds on buds, seeds, grain, fruit, insects, mushrooms, and occasional birds, but as cold weather approaches it concentrates on ripe nuts and acorns. These are buried separately in little holes, and apparently the squirrel finds them by memory and a keen sense of smell after they are buried under winter snow.

Squirrel nests may be in hollow trees, or built in the branches of trees. Those leaf-nests are composed of leafy twigs with an inner nest of grass. In early spring a litter of one to four young is born, and the mother may raise a second brood in late summer. Numerous enemies, including hawks, owls, foxes, bobcats, and man keep them from becoming too abundant. Squirrels contribute to forest conservation, for their uneaten stores of nuts and acorns sprout into new trees.

*The gray squirrel is a familiar species of city parks*

**Red Squirrel**
**Other Common Names** — Chickaree
**Scientific Name** — *Tamiasciurus hudsonicus*
**Family** — Sciuridae (marmots , squirrels, and chipmunks)
**Order** — Rodentia
**Size** — Body length, 11½ to 14 inches; tail, 4 to 5¾ inches; weight, 5 to 11 ounces
**Range** — North America south of the arctic limit of trees, south to mountainous regions of Idaho, Montana, and Wyoming in the west, and eastern North Dakota, Iowa, Indiana, and northern Ohio east to the Atlantic, farther south in mountains to North Carolina

## Habits of The Red Squirrel

The red squirrel, or chickaree, as it is often called, is such a versatile little animal that it is very difficult to judge its true character. By many of the country people who know it by sight but depend upon the bigoted statements of a few, it is believed to be a mischievous, thieving tyrant that should be destroyed at sight. No birds or squirrels, they say, are safe in the woods where the red squirrel resides. This is unfortunate, for it certainly is not the villain so often pictured.

Red squirrels are most entertaining and interesting animals. The have much more character than the gray squirrel and greatly surpass this squirrel in agility. The red squirrel is impulsive, impudent, and full of initiative, and possibly one's early association with them may play an important part in his admiration for red squirrels.

The old home, where one naturalist's boyhood days were spent, was about half a mile from Boonton, in northern New Jersey. The house and old cement barn with its accompanying sheds were surrounded by trees. In his yard and that of his neighbor's there were five huge chestnut trees, two shell-bark hickories, a number of pignut hickories, and two large butternuts. Both of these butternuts had hollow trunks, a wonderful place for squirrels to use for storing nuts and for hiding. On the northeastern side of the house were two large Norway spruce trees, whose long cones, filled with seeds, made excellent squirrel food. The property sloped sharply and to level it off for lawn, driveway, and garden, a series of stone walls had been built, some of which were eight or ten feet high. Those near the house had been laid with concrete, but those about the lower garden were dry walls, thus offering plenty of holes for squirrels to make their homes. There were always a number of red squirrels about the place, especially about the barn, and many families of squirrels had been reared under the wooden eaves.

In 1908 the first starlings the naturalist had ever found nesting used a hole made by the squirrels under these very eaves and raised two families, despite the fact that the squirrels were using the same eaves at the other end of the barn to bring up a family of their own. The naturalist spent many hours trying to tame some of these squirrels with varying success. Invariably, however, if he managed to gain the confidence of one, a neighbor's cat would capture it. It was always disappointing to lose a special pet in this way. Cats caught many of the red squirrels, especially when they were on the ground searching for fallen nuts, but their numbers did not seem to diminish.

One of the naturalist's earliest recollections was of sitting on one of the stone walls watching a red squirrel gathering the bark from a dead branch of a tulip tree and carrying it into a hole in the stone wall, about 30 feet from where he was sitting. Later he found a brood of young squirrels running about the wall, which led him to believe that the hole had been the entrance to a nursery. He seldom saw a gray squirrel near his home. To discover them he had to climb a half-mile to the ridge where the hickory trees grew more abundantly.

An occurrence of special interst to the naturalist, which placed a new insight on the gray squirrel and red squirrel association, took place at one of his neighbor's in the 1950's. The neighbor asked to borrow his extension ladder, as he wanted to investigate the contents of flicker nest box he had placed on one of his trees. He said that he was sure it contained the nest of a gray squirrel. He had heard a great commotion and discovered a gray and red squirrel in combat about the box's entrance. Investigation of the box showed that it contained five baby red squirrels, one of which was dead with a head wound; a second was still alive but it also had been bitten. There was no proof that the gray squirrel was the attacker. In the excitement, the red squirrel might have bitten her own children, but the gray was certainly the one that was the trespasser.

The three other young red squirrels appeared to be in good condition. Although very young, their eyes had but recently opened. It was necessary to feed them from a medicine dropper at first. The wounded one lived but a few days; the other three reached maturity. Two of the squirrels could be handled freely, but the third was a "little fiend" and bit at every opportunity. Even at this young age they showed their individual temperaments.

This same neighbor took a great interest in the small creatures about his home and had an extensive wildlife feeding station on the ground, which he maintained throughout the year. This station attracted many birds and squirrels. The main feeding receptacle was a large wooden platform about five feet square. It was held together by two 2 by 4 joists. Upon these the platform rested, leaving a four-inch open space between the boards and the ground. Slightly to one side of the center of the platform, there was a knothole about an inch and a half in diameter.

*Red squirrel*

*The red squirrel, or chickaree, lives in evergreen (coniferous) woodlands*

One day a red squirrel joined the numerous gray squirrels that come regularly to the station. A generous supply of grain and seeds had been spread upon the platform. Soon the gray squirrels began to gather until eight of them were feeding there and a red squirrel soon joined the group. The gray squirrels paid no attention to the red squirrel's arrival. The red worked his way to the center of the platform, tested a few sunflower seeds and then he set to work. With his front paws and nose he pushed a small pile of seeds ahead if him straight to the knothole and let them drop through the ground below. Then he went back for another supply. He worked diligently for a few moments

until he had accumulated a good supply beneath the platform. Then he went to the edge and ran underneath it where he could feed on the seeds by himself.

The red squirrel is the same behavioral type wherever it is found whether it is in the mountains of North Carolina and Tennessee—where it is known as the "mountain boomer"—or the Adirondacks, the north woods of Canada, the mountains of Alberta and British Columbia, or among the spruces of Alaska. Although the environment may change its habits in a small degree, everywhere it is the same curious, rollicking, and resourceful animal.

In the almost silent, snow-filled woods with the thermometer hovering near zero, one can pass through miles of forest, seeing never a mammal and only an occasional bird, such as a Canada jay. One feels very much alone in this vast world. If he sits down for a moment he is almost sure to hear the snickering of a red squirrel. A few squeaks on the back of one's hand (*see Attracting Birds by Sound, under Bird*), and before long the inquisitive little animal will be on a tree trunk by one's side. It does not want to make friends but its curiosity may bring it within arm's length. One moves on with a feeling of comradeship, knowing that other mammals are sharing the forest with him.

The red squirrel will defend its home range against heavy odds. A robin or a hummingbird will do the same. The red squirrel has a family to support and it is up to it to see that they are protected and live to go out into the world. It cares for no competition on its special grounds.

That the red squirrel is more carnivorous than the gray squirrel is suggested by the red squirrel s use of the suet fastened to trees at bird feeding stations. The red squirrels make daily visits to it, something that naturalists do not often see a gray squirrel do. After dark when the outside lights are turned on, one may often amuse himself by sitting a few feet from the suet-tree, watching the flying squirrels that also come to feed. From their intentness one would judge that they enjoy their repast just as much as the red squirrel enjoyed his but an hour or two before. The red squirrel is not our only carnivorous squirrel.

The red squirrel's diet occasionally includes the eggs and young of birds, but it certainly will *not* destroy every bird nest that it can find. The success of starling nesting in the old barn, the phoebes in the shed, and the many robin's nests in the Norway spruces at the naturalist' old home is testimony of this. It proves to him what other naturalists had discovered—that not all red squirrels acquire the nest-visiting habit. —T.D.C.

*Recommended Reading*

**Mammals of North America**—Victor H. Cahalane The Macmillian Company, New York.
**The Red Squirrel: Its Life History and Habits**—Robert T. Hatt, Roosevelt Wildlife Animals, Vol 2, College of Forestry, Syracuse, New York.

*How the Squirrel Got Its Name*

Naturalists of pre-Christian eras were well acquainted with a little rodent that spends much of its time leaping in trees. They did not consider that trait to be its most distinctive one, however. In regions where midday heat was oppressive for much of the year, men were fascinated that the nut-eater carried a built-in parasol. From *skia* (shade) plus *ouva* (tail), the little animal with the big tail was known to Greeks as the *skiuros*.

Its name passed through Latin and entered English prior to the 14th Century. Early writers used at least 15 different spellings, for the old word was ill-adapted to clumsy northern tongues. Eventually it was standardized as *squirrel*. Captain John Smith was incredulous when he saw the large size of Virginia squirrels. Writing in 1624, he declared that the largest were about the size of a small English rabbit.

Firmly established in many temperate regions, the squirrel is no longer noted for its equipment with which it was thought to shade itself from the sun. But the ancient title clings to it so firmly that in most parts of the world its name still has the meaning of *shady-tail*. —W.B.G.

**STARFISH**
**Common Starfish**
**Other Common Names**—Sea star
**Scientific Name**—*Asterias forbesi*
**Family**—Asteriidae (starfishes)
**Order**—Forcipulata
**Size**—Diameter, 6 to 11 inches
**Range**—Atlantic ocean, from Maine to Mexico

The common starfish of the Atlantic Coast is a creature of the shallows, from the shoreline to depths of about 90 feet. It is most common on rock bottoms, where oysters and mussels (*see under Bivalve*), the prey of the starfish, abound.

Members of this species customarily have five arms, although normal individuals with four, six, or even seven arms are sometimes found. The color is variable, and may be orange, green, purple, or brown.

Starfishes are echinoderms (*see Echinoderm*) in the phylum that also contains sea cucumbers, sea lilies, sea urchins, and others. All of them exhibit radial symmetry in fives, or multiples of five; from a central point, identical organs grow outward in five directions. Thus a starfish has five stomach pouches, five sets of sex organs, and five eyes (one at the tip of each arm).

The skeleton of the starfish is external. It is composed of tiny calcareous plates that hinge upon one another, combining a large measure of protection for the internal organs and also a high degree of flexibility. The skin covering the plates is studded with calcareous spines.

Each arm of the starfish has a small eye at its tip. From that point, a deep groove extends to the mouth, in the center of the under side. Within the groove are four rows of tube feet, each ending in a suction cup. The legs are operated by muscles that surround bulbs of water connecting with each foot; when the muscles contract, the water pressure in the bulb forces the leg to expand. The combined expansion and contraction of hundreds of tube feet carry the starfish on its slow course over the bottom.

To feed on an oyster or a mussel, the starfish crawls upon the shellfish, straps its arms about it, and pulls. When the oyster tires and permits the two valves to open, the starfish everts its stomach, and digestion takes place within the shell (*See account under Mollusk*). When it is complete, the stomach and its contents are drawn back by the starfish.

The regenerative powers of the starfish are well known. Cutting off one, two, or sometimes all of the arms does not kill the animal. It immediately commences to rebuild the lost portions, and eventually duplicates them exactly.

Other species of starfishes live in the Arctic, in the tropics, and in all oceans. The large Pacific starfish (*Pisaster*) is nearly a foot wide. The Atlantic sun star has 10 arms, and the sunflower star, from the South Pacific, has 20.

—G.B.S.

*Recommended Reading*

**Animals without Backbones**—R. Buchsbaum. University of Chicago Press, Chicago.
**Field Book of Seashore Life**—Roy Waldo Miner. G.P. Putnam's Sons, New York.

## STARLING

**Other Common Names**—None
**Scientific Name**—*Sturnus vulgaris*
**Family**—Sturnidae (starlings)
**Order**—Passeriformes
**Size**—Length, 7½ to 8½ inches
**Range**—Breeds throughout the United States, and north to Hudson Bay and south into Mexico. Winters in same areas

In spring the starling has a glossy sheen of green and purple. Its beak is yellow. During the winter months its beak is dark, its color is dulled, and it is heavily sprinkled with light spots. This species has a very short tail.

One of the most dramatic sights in nature is a mass of starlings arriving at an evening roost. Flock after flock of them, 300 to 400 at a time, swirl like a black snowstorm, spread fanwise, and pitch to unoccupied perches. Most of the flocks come from a long distance. The flight lines of these birds have been traced for at least 20 miles. The roost may be in a group of trees, on the eaves and ledges of large buildings, or, as at Riverside Drive and 125th Street in New York City, under and around bridges and viaducts.

*Starling,  spring plumage (above); winter plumage (below)*

In 1890, 80 starlings were brought over from Europe and set free in Central Park in New York City. In 1891, 40 more were liberated there. These 120 birds have now multiplied into many millions. The species has spread as far north as Hudson Bay, as far south as Florida and Mexico, and as far west as California and British Columbia. The expansion of its range has been more rapid in recent than in earlier years.

In a natural state, all forms of life live in a sort of wavering balance. One form depends on another as food and may in turn be fed on by something else. Each species tends to be a check on some other species. No one bird or mammal population gets far out of hand. But when a bird is introduced to a new environment, it usually does one of two things: It either dies out quickly, or, if its new home is suitable, as in the cases of the house sparrow and starling, it spreads rapidly. This is possible because it leaves behind, in its native land, those forces that tend to control its increase. Such forces include diseases, parasites, and the larger animals that feed on it. To insure its survival, it must displace other birds that compete with it for food and nesting sites.

Starlings select their nesting territory early and are prepared to hold it against all comers. Sometimes they nest in little colonies in old church towers and in corners of buildings, but they nest singly, too—wherever they can find a good natural cavity, a suitable birdhouse, or a woodpecker hole. The five to seven pale blue eggs are laid in a bulky but loose nest of grass and straw. The period of incubation is from 11 to 14 days. The young birds are dark gray during their first year. Sometimes two broods a year are raised.

Starlings eat a tremendous amount of insects that live on or in the ground. In summer as much as 90 percent of their food is made up of animal matter. In recent years the starling has become the most effective check of the Japanese beetle.

The starling's own notes are mostly squeaks, whistles, and chatterings, but it is an expert at imitating other birds. Some individual starlings are better imitators than others.

The starling is here to stay. It has thoroughly adapted to its new environment. It is normally a year-round resident, but birds in the extreme northern portion of the starling range move southward during winter.—A. B. Jr.

**STICKLEBACK** (*See Three-spined Stickleback under Fish: Some Common Freshwater Fishes of North America*)

## STILT
**Black-necked Stilt**
**Other Common Names**—Longshanks, lawyer
**Scientific Name**—*Himantopus mexicanus*
**Family**—Recurvirostridae (avocets and stilts)
**Order**—Charadriiformes
**Size**—Length, 15 inches
**Range**—Breeds from Oregon, Utah, and Colorado south to California, New Mexico, Texas, Louisiana, Florida, and casually in South Carolina. Winters from California to Louisiana southward

The black-necked stilt is white below and entirely black above, the line of demarcation being very distinctly drawn down each side of the neck. It is one of the largest shorebirds and has long, very slender red legs. The bill is long and delicately pointed.

The black-necked stilt is a characteristic bird of shallow sloughs, wet meadows, and grassy marshes of the western United States. It also lives around small ponds where it can run about in the shallow water. It is not abundant throughout its range, since suitable feeding places are few and scattered. Black-necked stilts are abundant in summer in the Mississippi Valley.

*Black-necked stilts*

About the alkaline lakes and ponds of the Great Basin, farther west, they are often seen with avocets. In some of the irrigated valleys of California, they are quite abundant.

In the breeding season black-necked stilts often gather in small groups of four to six pairs. The nests in the community are often placed within 15 or 20 yards of each other. The nest is formed of a small quantity of dried grasses, scarcely sufficient to protect the eggs from the wet marsh. As the eggs are incubated, however, the adults increase the size and height of the nest with dry twigs, roots, pondweeds, and other materials. The habit of adding new material to the nest after the female begins incubating is common to almost all birds that breed in marshes. Normally, four eggs are laid. They are a dark yellow or clay color, thickly marked with large blotches of black.

The males stay near the nest and drive away crows and blackbirds that happen to wander too close. Rapid and loud yippings indicate their alarm at the approach of large predators. When the young leave the nest, they follow their parents through the grasses. At the appearance of danger, they immediately squat and remain motionless. Their mottled plumage blends well with their surroundings.

The food of the black-necked stilt consists of small water snails, insects, worms, and the young fry of fishes.

In the eastern United States the black-necked stilt is uncommon. Recently, a few have been reported in southern New Jersey where the black-necked stilt was abundant during the early part of this century. However, hunting pressures and the disappearance of suitable nesting sites forced it to move westward.

Most black-necked stilts leave the United States in autumn, but a few remain along the Gulf Coast and in various parts of California.   —A. B., Jr.

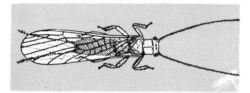

*Stonefly*

# STONEFLY
**Common Stonefly**
**Other Common Names**—Rockfly, troutfly
**Scientific Name**—*Neophrasganophora capitata*
**Family**—Perlidae (stoneflies)
**Order**—Plecoptera
**Size**—Length, one inch
**Range**—Worldwide

North America has about two hundred species of stoneflies. Adults, which usually rest on streamside vegetation, may scurry away when frightened instead of taking flight. All of them are thick-bodied, slow-moving insects that fly weakly on two pairs of wings; the larvae are aquatic, or water-dwelling on the bottoms of streams, chiefly in currents.

The first pair of wings of the adult is narrower than the second pair which usually has a lobe on the trailing edge. The wings are folded flat along the back when the insect is at rest. In the similar mayflies the wings are held upright, and the first pair of wings is larger than the second.

Adult stoneflies may appear at any time of the year from January to late fall, depending upon the species. Spring songbirds, such as phoebes, may feed heavily on adult stoneflies emerging in late winter or spring. Most of the adult stoneflies have no mouth parts, and cannot feed the males die after mating; the females after the eggs are laid in the water.

The larval stonefly is a nymph, a flat-bodied, six-legged water-dweller with long antennae and two long threadlike tails. Some nymphs are vegetarians; others are predaceous and feed on stream-bottom animals such as mayfly nymphs and the larvae of midges. The stonefly nymphs are eaten by the young of the larger dragonflies, and by salamanders, frogs, and turtles. They may live as nymphs for several seasons before becoming adult. Both adults and nymphs of stoneflies are major food items of bass, trout, crappies, and other freshwater game fishes (*See under Fish*).

—G.B.S.

**STORK** (*See Wood Stork*)

**STRAWBERRY**
**Wild Strawberry**
**Other Common Names**—Virginia strawberry
**Scientific Name**—*Fragaria virginiana*
**Family**—Rosaceae (rose family)
**Range**—Newfoundland to Alberta, south to Nova Scotia, New England, Georgia, Tennessee, and Oklahoma; in barely separable forms, westward and southwestward
**Habitat**—Fields, open slopes, and borders of woods
**Time of Blooming**—April to July (Northwest)

The white, five-petaled, many-stamened flower of the strawberry is a familiar plant of fields and roadsides. The three-parted leaves have sharply toothed margins. The leaves of the common cinquefoil, or five-finger, are often confused with those of the strawberry but the cinquefoil has a five-parted leaf. The showy petals and a ring of nectar attract insects that then become dusted with the abundant pollen which they carry to other blossoms for cross-fertilization.

The true fruit of the strawberry is not the berry but the little "seeds" embedded in the berry's surface. Nor are the "seeds" true seeds; they are *achenes*, which contain the seeds. The fleshy berry is the receptacle, greatly enlarged. Its growth has been stimulated by auxin, a plant hormone produced by developing seeds.

*Wild strawberry*

Strawberry plants are not wholly dependent on seeds to maintain their kind for they send out runners, prostrate stems, that root at their tips and thus produce new plants. The gardener takes advantage of this habit, cuts off the runners and plants them in freshly plowed ground thereby getting new plants to bear more fruit.

There are several species of wild strawberries. This one has round-pointed berries while some have pointed berries. These often tiny berries are very delicious and if one has the patience to gather them he will be richly rewarded, for their flavor far exceeds that of the cultivated varieties. Jam made from the wild forms is delicious.

Many wild creatures relish the strawberry, and help to disperse its seed by the route of their digestive tracts. Its leaves and berries are eaten by upland gamebirds, fur and game mammals, and small mammals. The berries are enjoyed by many songbirds; so much does the robin in particular love the strawberry that this songbird can be a nuisance around the cultivated varieties. The strawberry plants are eaten by some species of deer.

*The lake sturgeon sometimes attains weights of 300 pounds*

## STURGEON
### Lake Sturgeon
**Other Common Names**—Rock sturgeon, red sturgeon.
**Scientific Name**—*Acipenser fulvescens*
**Family**—Acipenseridae (sturgeons)
**Order**—Acipenseriformes
**Size**—Length, up to 55 inches; weight, 60 pounds. Sometimes up to 8 feet long and over 300 pounds in weight
**Range**—In North America, through the freshwater drainages of the Red River of the North Hudson Bay, and the St. Lawrence River, and southward in the Mississippi River drainage to northern Missouri and Alabama

The appearance of the lake sturgeon changes as the fish matures. When young, the fish's snout is very sharp and its body is lined with rough, spined bony plates. With age, the snout becomes somewhat blunter and the plates get smoother or fall off entirely. There is a single dorsal fin that is set back almost to the base of the tail fin. The tail fin is forked and its upper lobe is much longer than its lower lobe.

The lake sturgeon's back is either olive-yellow, blue-gray, or gray. Its sides are lighter and its belly is milk white or yellow-white. When the fish is young, several dusky blotches are present on the body.

There are several other sturgeons native to North America. Some of them live in the ocean but swim into fresh water to spawn. Members of this group include the shortnose, *Acipenser brevirostrum;* green, *Acipenser medirostris;* Atlantic, *Acipenser oxyrhynchus;* and white, *Acipenser transmontanus,* sturgeons.                          —M.R.

## SUCKER
There are so many different fishes in the sucker family, Catostomidae, that even a partial listing would serve little purpose. The white sucker is one of the most common suckers and has been chosen as representative of the group.

### White Sucker
**Other Common Names**—Sucker, common sucker, black sucker, slender sucker, mullet, whitehorse
**Scientific Name**—*Catostomus commersoni*
**Family**—Catostomidae (suckers)
**Order**—Cypriniformes
**Size**—Length, up to 20 inches; weight, 4 pounds
**Range**—In fresh water from the Mackenzie River to eastern Canada and southward to the Gulf of Mexico

The white sucker's body is long and cylindrical. Its head is large and its snout is blunt. The mouth is located on the underside of the snout, an adaptation to the fish's bottom-feeding habits. There are no teeth in the mouth but some are present in the throat. There is one dorsal fin, which has from 9 to 14 soft rays. The tail fin is moderately forked.

The white sucker's back is colored olive-slate to brownish-slate, the scales usually having darker margins. The sides are more silvery and the belly is white to milky white. During mating time the fish often becomes very dark in color and it is this characteristic that gives it one of its many common names, the black sucker. —M.R.

## SUMAC
### Staghorn Sumac
**Other Common Names**—Velvet sumac
**Scientific Name**—*Rhus typhina*
**Family**—Anacardiaceae (cashew family)
**Range**—Gaspe Peninsula, Quebec to southern Ontario and Minnesota. South through Nova Scotia and New England to Illinois, Iowa, North Carolina, and Kentucky
**Habitat**—Dry, gravelly, or rocky soils
**Leaves**—Compound, one to two feet long, usually with two dozen or so narrow, tapering, toothed leaflets, paler below; turning yellow, then scarlet in autumn
**Bark**—Smooth, gray, and "stitched," somewhat like birch or mountain ash
**Flower**—Upright heads of very small, yellow-green blossoms on terminal branches
**Fruit**—Tall, conical clumps of fuzzy dark red berries

The staghorn sumac is the largest species of the genus *Rhus* in eastern North America. This small tree grows to a height of about 30 feet and is easily identified by its short, stout branches that are covered with a dense coating of nettlelike hairs. The resemblance of these branches to the antlers of deer has given the tree its common name.

The cut twigs of staghorn sumac exude a gummy secretion that turns black upon contact with the air. Conspicuous upright clusters of bright red fruit, about seven inches high and three inches wide, make this tree a particularly outstanding one.

Other species of sumac include the

*Staghorn sumac*

smooth sumac, *Rhus glabra;* the dwarf sumac, *R. copallina;* and a series of poisonous species—poison ivy, *R. radicans;* poison sumac, *R. vernix;* and poison oak, *R. toxiodendron.* These species all contain an alkaloid that produces a burning rash on contact with human skin. All of these poisonous species have whitish drooping fruit, making them easily identifiable from the nonpoisonous sumacs (*See under Plant: Poison Ivy and other Poisonous Plants*).

Many species of gamebirds and songbirds utilize the fruit of the various species of sumac, including the poisonous ones, as winter food. The bright fruits of the staghorn sumac remain on the plant during winter and are eaten by ruffed grouse, prairie chickens, bluebirds, juncos, thrushes, and vireos among others. Even chipmunks, hares, and rabbits utilize the fuzzy seeds. In Michigan, 25 to 50 percent of the winter diet of cottontails consists of the fruit of sumac.
—G.A.B.

## SUN

### The Sun, Earth's Power Plant

In the city of Baalbek in Lebanon the ruins of an ancient temple are dedicated to the sun god, Baal. Like the inhabitants of Lebanon, most peoples have passed through a period of sun worship somewhere in their history, a circumstance that is not surprising. Men saw that the sun provided light and warmth; that when it was high in the heavens, crops flourished and they had plenty to eat; that when it sank lower in the southern sky, the land grew barren and the winds were cold. Christmastime, the period immediately following the winter solstice, was a season of festivity and rejoicing long before the Christian era, for it was then that the receding sun paused in its journey southward, hesitated, and then resolutely started northward again to bring a new season of growth and fruitfulness.

What the ancients perceived thus dimly, we now recognize with a far clearer understanding of its implications; namely, that the sun is earth's vast power plant, supplying both the power for industrial uses and the energy for plant and animal growth. The wind that turns the windmills and fills the vessels' sails; the falling stream that turns the waterwheels or generates that other powerful agent, electricity; the coal and gas and oil that heat the steam for turbines or operate internal combustion engines: All these owe their existence to solar radiation.

The reason is that the sun governs the weather. This in turn has an important influence on plant and animal life. We know that when the weather is too dry, plants wilt and die and animals then starve. Prolonged and recurrent droughts by destroying the plant cover, expose the soil to wind action (another phase of weather); and when the fertile topsoil has been blown away, leaving only the infertile subsoil, we have a new desert in place of pro-

ductive land. We know, also, that too much rain may cause floods that drown or wash away plant and animal life along its course and carry off the topsoil. Electrical storms are a frequent cause of forest fires. Hurricanes may level vast tracts of timber in a few hours' time. Cold, windy, or wet weather prevents insects from flying and so may interfere with pollination and the setting of fruit and seeds. Plant distribution (and consequently, to a certain extent, animal distribution) is limited by the length of the growing season—i.e., the period between the latest spring frost and the earliest frost in fall—and by the possible extremes of temperature and moisture (*See under Season*).

How does the sun control these meterological conditions? First let us consider winds. Wind is air movement on a large scale. When the sun heats the atmosphere, the warmed air naturally rises, its place being taken by cooler (and hence heavier) air that flows in from the polar regions, where the sun's rays, striking the earth at an angle, provide less direct heat; and thus air currents are set up. When these currents

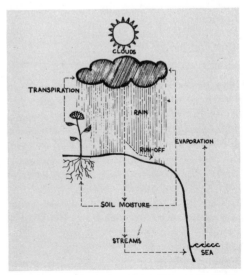

*The water cycle is a continous process of evaporation and condensation powered by the sun's heat*

attain sufficient velocity, they are perceptible as wind. There are other factors, of course, such as the earth's rotation and topography, that influence the force and direction of winds; but it is the sun that initiates the action. (*See under Wind*).

The sun is likewise responsible for falling rain and flowing streams. Were the sun to stop shining, the atmosphere, having shed its moisture in one last shower, would have no way of replenishing its supply, since without the sun's heat, evaporation from the oceans, rivers, lakes, and soil would cease. Without rain, the springs would dry up, and the last water in the streams would soon flow down to sea level and remain there. Such plants as had not already died from the cold and lack of light would then die of drought; and animal life could not long survive them.

The earth's surface, with its porous coat of vegetation, acts like a sponge, absorbing the rain as it falls and serving as a reservoir from which plant roots may drink through the sunny days to come. Some of this water is used by the plants to build new tissue or to make extra food for storage; the rest is given off by the leaves as vapor, mixing with the sunlit atmosphere and ultimately showing up as clouds, (*see under Cloud*) that in turn provide fresh showers to renew earth's water supply. This evaporation from the leaves, like that from the soil or from open bodies of water, is caused by the sun's heat.

In another way, too, solar influence has a bearing in general on storms and weather (*See under Weather*). On the bright surface of the sun there appear from time to time areas of lesser luminosity. These areas are known as sunspots. They are centers of violent disturbances and occur in definite cycles. Much work remains to be done on the subject, but a number of extremely interesting facts have already come to light. Periods of sunspot maximum are frequently accompanied by violent electrical storms, brilliant auroral displays, and serious radio and telephonic interference. Furthermore, there seems to be a direct relation between sunspot cycles and plant growth. The annual rings of trees provide a record of past weather, the width of the ring—the season's growth—being greater in wet than in dry years. Weather cycles thus determined show a remarkably close correlation with sunspot cycles. Thus we have another example of the influence of the sun on plant growth through weather. Indications of an even more remarkable effect of sunspots were recently discovered by R.H. Wheeler, of the University of Kansas, as a result of long-range studies of the history of psychology. He found that periods of idealism and nation-building alternated in definite, though sometimes intricate, cycles with periods of mechanism and civil strife. Comparing his human history cycles with the tree-ring weather cycles, he found an almost perfect correlation! Subsequent biological experiments supported Wheeler's theory that energies built up in cold periods flourish in succeeding warmer periods with a resultant golden age of constructiveness, but then decline during the hot years that follow, producing a period of laxity ending in wars as a new cold period begins. Here indeed is a striking example of solar influence.

Still another aspect of the sun's effect on living organisms is the role it plays in plant nutrition. Plants derive their nutrient elements from three sources: rain, soil, and air (*See under Plant*). Rain (whose recurrence, as we have seen, depends upon the sun) provides not only the much needed water, but also sulphur, carbon dioxide, and nitrogen in the readily available forms of ammonia and nitrates essential to plant growth. In the soil, rain water combines with the carbon dioxide given off by roots or decaying organic materials to form a weak acid that serves as a solvent for the soil minerals needed for plant growth. These enter the roots in solution and are borne thus to the parts of the plant where they are needed.

The sugars and starches manufactured by the plant must also be translocated in liquid form, the starch being converted to soluble sugars for this purpose. This sugar solution is what we have, in concentrated form, when we eat maple syrup. For the manufacture of starch the plant utilizes atmospheric carbon dioxide, which enters the leaves through the tiny pores, the *stomates*. Mingling with the water vapor present, it is there made into carbohydrates through the joint action of sunlight and green coloring matter, *chlorophyll*. This process of food-making is known as *photosynthesis*; literally, a putting together by means of light (*See under Chlorophyll*).

A very important aspect of photosynthesis is its effect upon animal life. When a plant or an animal breathes, it takes in free oxygen from the air and gives off carbon dioxide. Were this entirely a one-way process, the atmospheric oxygen would presently be used up, and life as we know it could not continue. Green plants aided by sunlight, however, reverse the process. For every molecule of starch or sugar manufactured from the otherwise useless carbon dioxide, a plant gives off a molecule of free oxygen, to be used again in respiration by plants and animals. Thus plants and sun, working together, help to purify the air for animals. Water plants perform a similar service for fishes and other aquatic animals, in that they aerate the water by thus giving off oxygen (*See Pond*).

Because of its effect on plant nutrition, the sun also affects flowering and fruiting. Blossoming occurs only when the ratio of carbohydrates to nitrogen content is relatively high; but it must not be too high, or no fruit will set. Since the manufacture of carbohydrates is directly dependent upon sunlight, the importance of length of day in relation to bloom and fruiting is evident. Some plants, like buttercups, which need a maximum of light, blossom when the days are longest; others, like cosmos, produce only leafy growth when exposed to long hours of light, coming into the bloom only as the days grow shorter, or when they are artifically shaded during part of the day. The internal processes of the plant determine under what conditions the proper ratio is attained in a given species; the sun provides these conditions, since length of day is the result of the inclination of the earth's axis toward or away from the sun.

Whatever affects plant growth also affects animal life. This is obvious in plant-eating species; it is equally true in the case of carnivores, even though the relationship is less direct. The flesh-eaters depend upon the plant-eaters for food. If the latter died out because plantlife had been totally destroyed, the carnivorous animals would have no recourse but to consume one another and so die out too (*See under Predation*).

Another more direct effect of the sun on animal life is its influence on health through the provision of vitamin D. The ancient tribes identified the sun god with the god of healing.

The temple of the sun god is in ruins. The pagan rites with which men worshipped there have long since been forgotten. Yet in many lands the day of the week for worship is still called Sunday; and an enlightened world is not unmindful of earth's indebtedness to her solar power plant. Men still turn their thoughts and faces sunward, and their telescopes and cameras too, in an effort to learn more about the nature of this nearest star. In laboratories, scientists are busy with innumerable experiments designed to show in ever greater detail the role of sunlight in plant and animal existence. Though the sun is but an average sort of star in our vast galaxy, to the earth it is by far the most important star of all.        —G.A.P.

*The sundew grows in sandy soils and peat bogs*

*Recommended Reading*

**Our American Weather**—George H.T. Kimble. Indiana University Press, Bloomington, Indiana.
**The Secret of the Southwest Solved by Talkative Tree Rings**—Andrew E. Douglas. *National Geographic Magazine*, December 1929.
**The Star Called the Sun**—George Gamow. Viking Press, New York.
**The Sun**—Karl Kiepenheuer. University of Michigan Press, Ann Arbor, Michigan.
**The Sun and the Welfare of Man**—Charles G. Abbot. Smithsonian Institution Series, Inc., New York.
**Sun, Earth, and Man**—George and Eunice Bischof. Harcourt, Brace, & World, Inc., New York.
**The Sun, the Wind, the Sea, and the Rain**—Miriam Schlein. Abelard-Schuman, Ltd., New York.

## SUNDEW
**Round-leaved sundew**
**Other Common Names**—None
**Scientific Name**—*Drosera rotundifolia*
**Family**—Droseraceae (sundew family)
**Range**—Labrador to Alaska, south to Pennsylvania and California, in mountains to Alabama
**Habitat**—Peat or moist acidic soils
**Time of Blooming**—June to August

A small red-leaved plant of sandy soils and peat bogs, the sundew is most remarkable for the unusual facility of trapping small insects on the sticky upper surface of the leaves. Digestive juices dissolve the soft parts of the insects, and their chemical components are used by the plant.

The sundew family is widespread, with numerous species occurring in Europe, Asia, and in moist and mountainous regions of North and South America (*See also under Plant*). —G.B.S.

## SUNFISH
The sunfish family, Centrarchidae, is one of the more important groups of North American freshwater fishes. It includes several of the most sought after of game fishes. There are some 30 species in the family and three of the following are best known (*See under Fish: Common Freshwater Fishes of North America*)

### Bluegill
**Othe Common Names**—Sun perch, bream, blue sunfish
**Scientific Name**— *Lepomis macrochirus*
**Family**—Centrarchidae (sunfishes)
**Order**—Perciformes
**Size**—Up to about 1 foot long and about 1½ pounds in weight
**Range**—Widely distributed throughout the eastern half of the United States. Found elsewhere due to successful introduction

The bluegill's dorsal fin is typical of the sunfish family. It has spiny rays in front, the last of which is joined to the first of several soft rays in back. The anal fin is similar in structure.

*Bluegills*

Perhaps the most unusual thing about the bluegill is its great variation in color. Its overall coloring may be anything from pale blue to a lustrous orange. Most commonly, however, it is dark olive-green, with a lavender sheen on its sides. Sometimes the gill covers are bright blue, hence the fish's common name. There are six to eight dark vertical bars on the sides of the fish. The throat, and sometimes the belly and lower part of the tail, may be orange or yellow. There is a dark blotch on the rear of the dorsal fin.

The favorite foods of the bluegill are insects and their larvae. The fish will eat many things, however, and will even consume plants when no animal foods are available. Although fairly small, bluegills are favorites of anglers, for they are fine panfish.

**Largemouth Bass**
**Other Common Names**—Black bass, largemouth, green bass, slough bass, lake bass, Oswego bass
**Scientific Name**—*Micropterus salmoides*
**Family**—Centrarchidae (sunfishes)
**Order**—Perciformes
**Size**—Length, in northern states, up to about 2 feet; weight, 9 pounds; in southern states, much larger and weights of about 25 pounds may be attained
**Range**—Throughout entire eastern half of the United States and in parts of Canada and Mexico. Artificially introduced elsewhere

The dorsal fin of the largemouth bass is divided almost in two. The front section is composed of 9 to 13 hard rays and arches down sharply before joining the rear section, which has 12 or 13 soft rays.

The color of the fish is fairly variable but is usually dark green on the back with lighter sides that are mottled with dark blotches. The belly is white with a green tinge and, sometimes, a tint of yellow or pink. (Young largemouth bass are more brightly colored and have larger eyes than do adults.) The mouth extends back beyond the rear of the eyes making it noticeably large, thus giving the fish its common name.

The largemouth bass eats a wide variety of foods, including other fishes, crayfishes, insects, and frogs. The largemouth is a fine fighter when hooked and has always been a favorite of sportsmen. The "bass" portion of its name is a misnomer for the fish is not a member of the true bass family, Serranidae (*See under Bass*).

**Smallmouth Bass**
**Other Common Names**—Bronzeback, northern smallmouth, red-eyed brass
**Scientific Name**—*Micropterus dolomieui*
**Family**—Centrarchidae (sunfishes)
**Order**—Perciformes
**Size**—Length, up to about 2 feet and 7 pounds in weight
**Range**—From Quebec, Canada, southward to northern Alabama and eastern Oklahoma. There has been extensive introduction of this fish into other areas of North America

The smallmouth bass looks very much like the largemouth bass and is often

*Largemouth bass (above); smallmouth bass (below)*

confused with it. Its dorsal and anal fins are almost exact duplicates of those described for the largemouth. It is the mouth of the smallmouth that makes it easy to distinguish between the two fishes. The mouth cuts back only to the center of the eyes in the smallmouth bass whereas it cuts back past the rear margin of the eyes in the largemouth bass.

The back and sides of smallmouth bass are golden green with light olive blotches. Five olive-green bars radiate back from the eyes and one similar bar runs from the eyes to the snout.

The diet of the smallmouth bass consists mostly of other fishes, crayfishes, and insects. The smallmouth is popular with anglers and, like the largemouth, is not a true bass. —M.R.

# SWALLOW

The graceful, swooping flight of the swallows and their cheerful twittering have made these birds welcome, especially when their annual migration brings them north to announce the arrival of spring.

Swallows are placed in the order Passeriformes, the huge group that contains the small perching birds. They have no close relatives within this group, however, as their specializations for spending most of the daylight hours in flight are not matched nor approximated by other species. The swifts, similar in appearance, differ anatomically; resemblances between swallows and swifts are due to adaptations to a similar way of life (*See Adaptations of Birds*).

Swallows are small birds; their necks are short, heads broad, tails full, wings long and narrow, and their bills are very short but exceptionally wide. Their feet are tiny and weak, and they have short legs. They feed on insects that they scoop from the air as they sweep over meadows, croplands, and ponds. They have bills fringed with bristles that assist in trapping their prey.

Of the seven swallows in the United States and Canada, two build their nests of mud, on cliffs or on man-made structures. One is the barn swallow, *Hirundo rustica*, a familiar species over much of the continent. It is the only swallow with the long, forked, swallow-tail, and the only one with reddish-buff underparts. The other species that builds a mud nest is the cliff swallow, *Petrochelidon pyrrhonota*, a manufacturer of gourd-shaped mud nests with a side entrance in contrast to the open cup nest of the barn swallow. This bird has a square-cut tail, white underparts, and a dark throat. The best field mark is a unique buffy patch on its upper rump.

Two swallows nest at the end of burrows that they dig in sandbanks. Bank swallows, *Riparia riparia*, often establish colonies. It is a small, brown bird with a notched tail and a dark brown band across its white underparts. The rough-winged swallow *Stelgidopteryx ruficollis*, is slightly larger and somewhat lighter, without a chest band, and with a dusky throat. This is the famed swallow of Capistrano. The eastern birds are just as regular in their springtime return to colonial sites.

The violet-green swallow, *Tachycineta thalassina*, the tree swallow, *Iridoprocne bicolor*, and the purple martin *Progne subis*, are cavity nesters; once they were dependent upon finding old woodpecker holes or natural cavities but now they use birdhouses (*See under Martin: Purple Martin.*) The violet-green swallow is a western bird ranging from Alaska through Mexico, and east to the Dakotas and Nebraska. It is shiny green and violet above, with white patches on the side of its rump and more white on its face than on the tree swallow. The tree swallow is more blue above than green, and does not have white rump patches. It ranges throughout southern Canada and the northern United States. Both of these birds have notched tails, as does the purple martin which is the largest of the North American swallows. It measures up to 8½ inches long. Males are glossy purple-black, while females are gray underneath. The purple martin nests along the Pacific Coast, southern Canada, and the eastern United States to the Gulf Coast.

All of the swallows return each year to the nesting site of the previous season, and the young to the place where they were raised. In general, only when all the available nesting places have been taken in an area will homeless couples strike off into new country.

In migration, swallows tend to move in huge, loose flocks sometimes numbering in the thousands. They roost together, often on telephone wires, frequently several species together. Purple martins spread out in flight more than the others, with two or three birds in sight at one time, all part of a great

*Tree swallows line up on the wires of a telephone pole for fall migration*

*Bank swallows nest in holes that may extend into the soil for two or three feet*

**Sizes**—Length, 5 to 5½ inches
**Range**—Nests from Alaska and north-western Canada east to Labrador and Newfoundland, south to southern United States. Winters in South America

This North American swallow closely resembles the rough-winged swallow. These two species differ from other North American swallows in lacking a metallic luster. The bank swallow, however, may be distinguished from the rough-winged swallow by the presence of a conspicuous brownish-gray band across its breast. It is not so generally distributed as some of the other swallows, its occurrence depending largely upon the presence of desirable nesting sites. Most swallows of the eastern United States more or less have changed their nesting habits since the arrival of the white man, but the little bank swallow continues to dig its horizontal holes in the banks of rivers, ponds, or lakes. Sometimes railroad cuts or other artificial banks are used, but sites near water are much preferred. In such situations it often nests in populous colonies where hundreds of birds may be seen skimming over the water or fields, catching small flying insects, or entering or leaving their excavations.

They often congregate in considerable numbers on telephone or telegraph wires, or along streams, just before their southward migration. The nest is two to three feet from the entrance of a hole in a bank. From four to six white eggs are laid.

wave of birds that may take hours to pass.                                    —G.B.S.

**Bank Swallow**
**Other Common Names**—Sand swallow, sand martin
**Scientific Name**—*Riparia riparia*
**Family**—Hirundinidae (swallows)
**Order**—Passeriformes

**Barn Swallow**
**Other Common Names**—Barn-loft swallow, fork-tailed swallow
**Scientific Name**—*Hirundo rustica*
**Family**—Hirundinidae (swallows)
**Order**—Passeriformes
**Size**—Length, 6 to 7½ inches
**Range**—Breeds from northwestern Alaska and central Quebec south to southern California, Mexico, southern Texas, and North Carolina. Winters from New

*Barn swallo*

Mexico to southern South America

The barn swallow is one of the favored group of birds that has multiplied its legions since the coming of the settlers to the North American continent. Although it nested over a vast area, from Mexico to Alaska, it was probably distributed rather thinly, originally nesting in caves along the coast, in mountain cliffs, and in hollows of gigantic forest trees. The proper nesting facilities must have been the chief limiting factor of this species in the early days. The plains and prairies, though abounding in insect food, offered no nesting sites until farms began to dot their flat expanses. Now the barn swallow is an abundant and familiar bird there. On the sandy, barren islands of the coast, they occurred only in migration until Coast Guard stations and beach cottages were built. Rocky caves on the New England coast were abandoned for fishing shacks. However, they still nest in their original haunts in a few spots in the West.

Barn swallows often gather in large groups around ponds or streams and weave an intricate aerial pattern over their surfaces, feeding on the dancing insects. They can be distinguished from other swallows by their deeply forked tails which show some white spots. The other swallows have notched or square tails. The underparts vary from a pale buff to a rich cinnamon—always deepest on the throat.

Barn swallows are colonial. They do not have the territorial conflict that exists among most other small birds. They are strong, swift fliers, able to cover a mile in less than two minutes; their food supply is not found on the ground or among the foliage, but is a moving one that must be sought far

*Barn swallow*

*Traveling at a speed of 40 miles an hour, the barn swallow migrates rapidly in fall*

and wide. There is no need, therefore, of defending a piece of ground in the immediate neighborhood of the nest.

Barn swallow nests are constructed of distinct layers of mud, each layer made up of small pellets which the bird has gathered in its bill. The layers are each separated by dry grasses. The interior of the cup is covered with a lining of soft feathers often from the nearest chicken yard.

The four to six speckled white eggs are incubated for a period of 11 to 13 days. The young remain in the nest longer than those of most small birds—16 days or so. They are constantly guarded and should an intruder approach the nesting area, the soft musical twitterings of the parents would change abruptly to a shrill *keet! keet!* as they dive and harass the trespasser.

The youngsters exercise their wings from the rim of the nest until they are ready to fly; they do not leave prematurely as young robins do but are capable of successful flights from the very start. It is not long before their flight becomes as accurate, swift, and graceful as that of their parents from which they can scarcely be distinguished except for their whiter breasts and less deeply forked tails.

Later in the summer, when the second brood has left the nest, large groups of swallows congregate on the ridgepoles of barns and along telephone wires. Arrival from other localities swell their ranks until they take off in a body for the South. By late July, multitudes of swallows are already on the move. Some cut crosscountry toward the coast and follow the outer beaches with the hordes of tree swallows. Others file down the interior valleys. They are daytime migrants, although on clear mornings they can sometimes be heard flying about before it is light enough for them to be seen. Some spend the night in the holes in sandbanks made by bank swallows.

At a direct-flight cruising speed of nearly 40 miles per hour, it does not take long to reach the wintering grounds in Central and South America, either by way of Mexico or the West Indies. Some stragglers, however, can be seen moving southward along the coast as late as November. In the spring they return as soon as enough insects are flying about to sustain them—about mid-April in the northern parts of the United States. —A. B., Jr.

**Cliff Swallow**
**Other Common Names**—Eave swallow, mud swallow, Republican swallow
**Scientific Name**—*Petrochelidon pyrrhonata*

*Cliff swallows pause to preen themselves during their southward flight*

**Family**—Hirundinidae (swallows)
**Order**—Passeriformes
**Size**—Length, 5 to 6 inches
**Range**—Nests from Alaska and Yukon to central Saskatchewan, east to Ontario and Quebec, south to Tennessee, Kentucky, Alabama, western North Carolina, and Texas. Winters in South America

Like most members of the family, this interesting and graceful swallow enjoys a wide distribution. The distinguishing marks are the brown upper tail coverts, the whitish forehead, and the square tail, which serve to identify it at any time. It is a general favorite among bird lovers in those localities that are fortunate enough to have it as a citizen. It, how-

*The cliff swallow has a white patch on its forehead and a short, square tail*

ever, is very local in distribution and in many communities where it was formerly abundant it is now scarce. It is associated in the minds of many with pleasant rural scenes where the bottle-shaped mud nests are plastered on the ends of rafters under the eaves of barns and other outbuildings. To others, in the more rugged West and North, it is recognized by these same nests which are attached to the faces of cliffs.

The cliff swallow, like its relatives, is a graceful forager of the air and consumes enormous quantities of insects, many of which are injurious to man's crops. Its powers of flight are very great, and hour after hour it may be seen sweep-

*Although tree swallows usually nest in tree hollows, they will utilize bird houses*

ing through the skies in endless, billowy flight.

From four to five white eggs speckled with rufous-brown, are laid.

**Tree Swallow**
**Other Common Names** — White-breasted swallow, blue-backed swallow
**Scientific Name** — *Iridoprocne bicolor*
**Family** — Hirundinidae (swallows)
**Order** — Passeriformes
**Size** — Length, 5 to 6 inches
**Range** — Nests from Alaska to Mackenzie and southern Canada, east to Labrador and Newfoundland, south from Canada along Pacific Coast to southern California and interior United States and eastern United States. South from New England to Tennessee and Missouri, west to Kansas, Utah, Nebraska, North and South Dakota, Colorado, and Wyoming. Winters from southern California, Arizona, and New Mexico, east to Virginia, and occasionally north to coastal Massachusetts and Long Island, New York

When the blustery days of March are over and milder April brings fresh ar-

rivals among the birds, there comes, leisurely drifting before the warm south wind, the advance guard of the great army of tree swallows. Their pure white breasts offer an easy field mark and at once distinguish them from other swallows. They migrate solely by day and their flight is usually more leisurely than that of other members of the family. Lazily and gracefully dipping and circling, they move forward in broad, streaming lines.

Immediately after the nesting season they begin to gather in ever-increasing numbers, myriads often flocking together preparatory to the southward migration. Before this flight begins they spend the weeks of late summer and early autumn foraging widely about the countryside. Often at dusk great numbers may be seen swirling down out of the sky and dropping noiselessly into the reeds. When the southward movement is well under way, great flights often are to be noted along the coasts of the southern states.

The nest is usually in a hollow tree, of grasses and feathers. From four to seven white eggs are laid.

*Multitudes of tree swallows are often seen in southern states during migration*

## SWAMPS AND MARSHES

Where the river makes its big bend, through the flat country of the town, there was quite a marsh. They say it was a lot more extensive before the water was drained off—some of it to make onion fields. The local bird-watcher's club and the school children were glad that some of it still remained, for it was by all odds the best spot for birds and other wildlife they knew. There was talk from time to time of draining the rest of the marsh. Some people said it was an eyesore, others that it bred mosquitoes. The bird-watchers and children did not share the view that it was an eyesore; to them it was a beautiful place, especially in the early morning when the rising sun dispersed the thin mists from the sparkling reeds and grasses. As for mosquitoes, the puddles around the farms and in the vacant lots around town bred just as many. It would be better to clean those up.

To think of losing the river marsh was an unpleasant thought, yet it was always a possibility. Where would the red-winged blackbirds go, and the bitterns and the rails? They would probably try to find other marshes, but wouldn't those marshes already have as many bird inhabitants as they could take care of? That was something to think about.

### What Is a Swamp?—A Marsh?

What is the difference between a swamp and a marsh? Some people are quite certain they are the same thing, —any low piece of muddy ground, saturated or partly covered with water. A swamp is wet, spongy land dominated by trees and shrubs. A marsh, on the other hand, is wet *treeless* land, characterized by cattails, sedges, and grasses. There are two very different kinds of marshes—those along the seacoast that are flushed by the tide, the salt marshes; and the ones that are fed by fresh water, the freshwater marshes.

*A typical swamp landscape*

The bird, animal, and plant life in these two types are quite different (*See under Marsh*).

## The Water Table

Some of the rain and snow that falls on the earth sinks into the ground. It sinks down into the subsoil and porous rocks where it forms a sort of underground reservoir where water is stored. The upper level of this is called the *water table*. This underground water finds its way eventually to plant roots or comes to the surface as bubbling springs, or flows into pools or lakes in the hollows. Often where it comes to the surface there are swamps and marshes. The heavy vegetation holds the water there, where it acts as a feeder and a stabilizer to the underground water supply or to nearby streams. In flood times, marshes and swamps are very helpful. When too much water arrives at the same place at the same time, floods occur. Marshes and swamps do their bit in preventing this. The waters gather in the low wet pockets and are slowed up by the heavy spongy vegetation. If there were more marshes, many floods would not be so disastrous (*See under Bog*).

## Swamps, Marshes, and Wildlife

When a bird student looks for warblers in the spring, he goes to his favorite wooded swamp, a piece of wooded land along a creek bottom. There the warbler hordes are most abundant. More different kinds of birds can be seen in a day in a swamp than in any other type of habitat (*See under Muskeg*). As for marshes, a good wet marsh is a bird-lover's idea of heaven. There is nothing he enjoys more than slopping around such a marsh in his rubber boots. There are rails, marsh wrens, bitterns, gallinules, coots, ducks, and many other birds. The botanist finds the rich vegetation of marshes and swamps always exciting. There are new things to be found, no matter how long he searches. The hunter, the trapper, and the fisherman would hate to see the marshes and swamps go, for it would mean the end of much of their recreation.

As a home for wildlife, and as a stabilizer of water, the value of swamps and marshes runs into many millions of dollars each year. Some people claim that the value is actually many *hundreds of millions of dollars*. It is difficult to put an accurate price tag on natural resources.

## Marshes Are Going. . .Going

It is said that every day plans are being made somewhere in this country to drain a lake, swamp, or a marsh. This cannot go on forever, for there will be no swamps or marshes left. The records show that between 80 million and 100 million acres of land have been drained in the United States for argiculture alone. This means that millions of acres of water have been hurried off the land, hurried to the sea before their time, before they have been of enough use to plants, beasts, birds, or man.

## Why Is Drainage Done?

Some people like the countryside to look neat and tidy like a city park or an estate. They think swamps are ugly. They itch to do something about them; to have them cleaned up if for no other reason than to get rid of them. These are the people who dislike to get their feet wet, who prefer to see the countryside from the comfort of an automobile.

Marshes and swamps are also drained for more practical reasons. Millions of acres are drained to make more land for farming. Other millions of acres are drained with the intention of controlling mosquitoes. These last two things seem worthy enough, but are they always?

## Does Agricultural Drainage Always Accomplish Its Purpose?

Oftentimes, when a piece of land has been drained, the rich black soil is excellent for farming but this is not always true. Millions of acres that have been drained have been without benefit to argiculture at all. The soil was not good or it had too much of an alkali content; or, in the case of many shallow lakes that have been drained, they have turned into peat bogs that are quite useless for farming. Then, too, even if the soil is good for farming, sometimes the water table drops so low that the plants have difficulty in picking up the water from the soil. There is a limit to which roots can penetrate.

### And Mosquitoes?

In similar manner, mosquito control does not always eliminate mosquitoes. Undoubtedly it often does but many swamps, marshes, and lakes are drained simply because they look like places that would breed mosquitoes, even though they may have no mosquitoes at all.

Malaria, which is carried by mosquitoes, is a menace, but millions of dollars have been appropriated for malaria control in states and communities where malaria does not exist. This is all very stupid; not only is the money spent uselessly but there is an even greater financial loss through the destruction of wildlife and the lowering of the water table. It is a double-headed loss.

### What Does Drainage Do to the Water Table?

Swamps and marshes are where the general water table reaches the surface of the ground, where the land is low enough so that the water seeping out collects in the pockets. If long ditches were cut from a marsh to the nearest stream the water would run out. As the water ran out of the ditch more water would feed into the marsh from the underground storehouse. This would

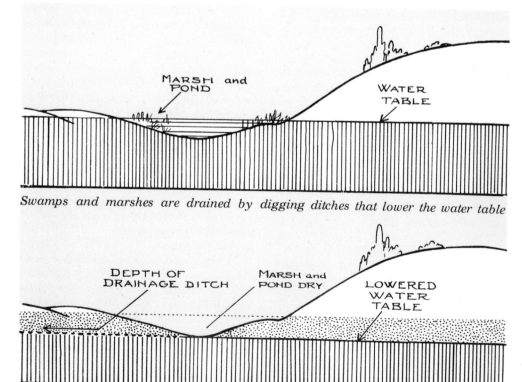

Swamps and marshes are drained by digging ditches that lower the water table

run out of the ditch, too, until not only the marsh was dry but the underground water had become so low that it would no longer feed the marsh.

In some prairie regions of the United States it is said that the underground water table has been lowered 50 feet or more in the last 30 years. When the water table become so very low it does not do much good to the plants that live on the ground surface. They can no longer pick up the moisture readily, and they become sickly and dry up.

Streams that seep out from the swamps or that are fed by the moisture from wetlands become very low or disappear when the swamps and marshes are destroyed. When streams become low or dried up, no longer can people go canoeing, fishing, or swimming.

In many places ponds and even lakes have gone down or have disappeared because the low swamplands around them were drained. Sometimes the drained swamplands become so dry that long, smoldering fires start. Fires of this kind rage in the Florida Everglades and in other swamps that have been drained and have become dried out. The feeding grounds of the herons and ibises in times of great fires in the Everglades go up in smoke. Much of the Everglades have been drained for farming.

It is not a pleasant picture to think that some day all the marshes of America might be gone. If such a day came, man might find his water supply getting low and his crops failing. Swamps help hold the world together just as do streams and rivers.

### Drainage and Wildlife

Waterfowl are much less abundant today than they were a generation ago. The breeding grounds are greatly reduced. The few ducks that do try to nest in ditched marshes have a hard time. Food is meager and the ditches are a trap for the young; the sides are so steep they cannot climb out. Occasional fires that sweep the dry marshes burn the eggs and fledglings. In some marshes where the water has become too low, waterfowl sometimes fall prey to diseases such as botulism (*See Botulism*). Then, too, hunters with automobiles can get to the few remaining good spots much more easily than they could years ago. It is not an encouraging picture for the ducks. The federal government has created a large number of national wildlife refuges but this only solves part of the problem.

Malheur Lake, in southern Oregon, one of the greatest nesting places for waterfowl on the continent, was drained during the 1930's. The homes of myriads of birds were destroyed. The lakes became a worthless desert, useless for both farming and for birds. Fortunately, after this costly mistake the waters have again been turned into Malheur and the birds are returning. But the money squandered is gone forever.

### What To Do?

The drainage of marshes still goes on, but now there is also some money being spent to restore swamps. In some places the water table is being raised and marshes are becoming healthy again. The fires are dying out and the birds are beginning to nest as they formerly did. Even the surrounding fields and woodlands are becoming healthier.

There will probably continue to be a certain amount of drainage and mosquito control. But there should be a careful study of each marsh before it is drained. If drainage is shown to be necessary, the methods used should be such that the destruction to wildlife will be minimized.

In mosquito control, there are practical methods that do not require ditching the marsh and letting the water out. There are small fishes and other natural enemies that will eat the mosquito larvae. The water areas can be enlarged with ponds so that the constant movement of water will destroy the mosquito wigglers. There are volatile poisons, such as pyrethrum, which are not harmful to wildlife, but which destroy the mosquitoes. It is possible to control mosquitoes and still have the marshes healthy enough for breeding of wild ducks and other marshbirds. Marshes in which there are no mosquitoes should not be tampered with of course.

How much better everything would be if man would try to understand and adjust himself to nature instead of constantly fighting it.                —R.T.P.

## SWIM BLADDER (*See under Fish*)

## SWAN

Swans are the largest of all waterfowl. The two native North American swans are the whistling swan and the trumpeter swan. The mute swan has been introduced into the eastern and middle western United States and now nests in the wild largely in Michigan and southeastern New York State.

The commonest wild swan of North America, the whistling swan, *olor columbianus,* is smaller than the rare trumpeter swan, *Olor buccinator.* It is about 52 inches long and weighs about 16 pounds. Like the trumpeter, it has a black bill, usually with a small yellow mark in front of the eye. Young birds (cygnets) are brownish, with pale pink bills that show no black at the margin of the face.

Whistlers nest in the Arctic, in the bleak islands north of the continental mainland south to the Alaskan Peninsula. They winter along the saltwater bays of the Atlantic Coast, and on western lakes and rivers as far south as Yellowstone Park, in Wyoming, and in Utah, and the San Joaquin Valley in California.                —G.B.S.

### Saving the Trumpeter Swan

In 1919, much to the delight and surprise of conservationists, a few pairs were discovered nesting in Yellowstone National Park. These birds owed their

*Trumpeter swan*

existence to the Lacey Act of May 7, 1894, which established wildlife protection in the park, thereby protecting the forebears of the 1919 swans.

Unfortunately, the Lacey Act did not prevent the extirpation of the trumpeter swan over most of its breeding range in the United States. Even a second Lacey Act in 1900, the Weeks-McLean law of 1913 and the Migratory Bird Treaty Act of 1918, could not prevent that disaster.

In his book, *The Trumpeter Swan,* Winston E. Banko describes the efforts of Americans to protect the few remaining trumpeters through legislation:

"For two decades after 1900, a number of prominent American scientists interested in the problems of species survival commented on the fate of the trumpeter swan. William T. Hornaday reported that in 1907 these swans were regarded as so nearly extinct that a doubting ornithological club of Boston refused to believe on hearsay evidence that the New York Zoological Park contained a pair of the living birds, and a committee was appointed to investigate in person and report.

"Edward Howe Forbush, the eminent ornithologist, lamented:

'The trumpeter has succumbed to incessant persecution in all parts of its range, and its total extinction is now only a matter of years. . . .The large size of this bird and its conspicuousness have served, as in the case of the whooping crane, to make it a shining mark, and the trumpetings that were once heard over the breadth of a great continent, as the long converging lines drove on from zone to zone, will soon be hear no more.

"Passage of the Migratory Bird Treaty Act six years later placed a closed season on both species of native swans for the first time when it became effective in 1918. This was the first aid to survival of the few trumpeters that still existed outside Yellowstone Park boundaries and that were to be so important in the eventual restoration of the species.

"In 1929 the Migratory Bird Conservation Act authorizing the acquisition of land for waterfowl refuges was passed by Congress. When supported with funds in 1934, this basic waterfowl legislation was as important in provid-

*Trumpeter swans often nest on muskrat lodges*

*Two trumpeter swans soar over Red Rocks National Wildlife Refuge, Montana*

ing for the future increase of the United States trumpeter flock as the Migratory Bird Treaty Act was in protecting the remnant populations.

"Under the Migratory Bird Conservation Act, the Red Rock Lakes Migratory Waterfowl Refuge in southwestern Montana was established by Executive Order in 1935. This area, containing thousands of acres of historic trumpeter swan breeding habitat, was subsequently staffed by the Biological Survey, a predecessor of the United States Fish and Wildlife Service.

"The 22,682-acre area originally set aside under this order was enlarged in September of the same year, when about 18,000 additional acres were included in the refuge in order to complete the breeding-ground acquisition and to bring under management certain warm spring-water areas important to the swans during the winter months.

"Although several management problems remained, the establishment of this refuge provided the upward turning point for this species in the United States. While the status of the trumpeters in Yellowstone Park before the establishment of the refuge was marginal, it was apparently improving slowly. But the existence of this species outside the park was actually in jeopardy by the early 1930's.

"Later, since it was discovered that irresponsible waterfowl hunters were killing swans under the claimed pretext of shooting snow geese, the hunting seasons on snow geese were closed in those states within the trumpeters' winter range. Service regulations, stemming from authority in the Migratory Bird Treaty Act, closed the snow goose season first in the state of Idaho in 1941, and were modified about a decade later to exclude the counties where swan shooting was not a problem.

"In Montana the snow goose closure has been in continuous effect in Beaverhead, Gallatin, and Madison counties, from 1942 until the present. Similar Federal closures were initiated as a statewide measure in Wyoming in 1946 because of the threat posed to the newly

*Trumpeter swan from Audubon's* Elephant Folio

established trumpeter flock introduced to National Elk Refuge in Jackson Hole; however, these regulations were modified in 1955 to include only the pertinent areas of Teton and Lincoln counties.

"Unless these protective measure had been taken by the federal government, this large and conspicuous bird would surely have disappeared from its native breeding grounds in this country." (*See also under Extinct and Vanishing Animals of North America*)

*Recommended Reading*

**The Trumpeter Swan—Its Life History, Habits, and Population in the United States**—Winston E. Banko. North American Fauna No. 63, U.S. Government Printing Office, Washington, D.C.

**SWEET GUM** (*See under Gum*)

**SWIFT**
**Chimney Swift**
**Other Common Names**—Chimney swallow, American swift
**Scientific Name**—*Chaetura pelagica*
**Family**—Apodidae (swifts)

**Order**—Apodiformes
**Size**—Length, 5 to 5½ inches
**Range**—Breeds in eastern North America from central Alberta, southeastern Saskatchewan, Manitoba, southern Quebec, and Newfoundland, south to Florida and the Gulf Coast, and west to central Montana, Wyoming, and eastern Texas. Winters over the Amazon Basin forest of South America

The chimney swift is distinguished from the swallows by its long, thin wings that flicker like a bat, and do not seem to beat in unison. It appears as if the wings beat alternately, but films show conclusively that the swift's wings beat together, the way all other birds' wings do. In its headlong flight, the chimney swift streamlines itself so much that it resembles a little bow and arrow, or a "cigar with wings," as more than one naturalist has called it. It seems to have no tail at all, except when it turns or banks, then it spreads its spiny-tipped tail feathers wide, like a little fan.

By early May large flocks of chimney swifts gather together at their evening roosts. Through the day they fly about individually, or in little groups, in search of food, but toward dusk they come by the hundreds, and sometimes thousands, to spend the night in the same chimney or other communal roost.

Before they descend, they mill about in a wide circle. The birds all fly in the same direction, round and round. This is usually referred to as the "dance of the chimney swifts." The swirling ring narrows down, sweeps closer to the open top of the chimney, and then one bird, holding its wings in a V high over its back, drops into the gaping hole. Another follows, than three or four plunge in at a time. At first it does not seem to affect the mass of the whirling birds very much, but it is not long before they begin to pour into the chimney in a steady black stream. In a few minutes, only a few stragglers are left in the air. The chimney swifts cling to the sooty walls, using the sharp nails of their toes to hold on and their stiff spiny tails to brace them. They roost in rows and clusters, lapping one over the other, like thatch or shingles on a roof.

Although chimney swifts roost in large numbers, they usually nest in individual pairs, one to a chimney. Their nest is plastered to the side of the bricks, several feet from the top (anywhere from 2 to 20 feet down). It is a little wickerwork shelf made of dead twigs which the swift, hesitating in its flight, snaps from the tips of tall trees. These twigs are pasted together with a glue made from the bird's saliva.

Originally, when swifts did not have chimneys to build in, they used hollow trees and caves. Today, if they can't find a suitable chimney, they will also use the inside of a cabin or a barn wall, as phoebes and barn swallows do. The four to six eggs are pure white. For 19 days both parents incubate them, changing places on the nest every 20 minutes or half hour, day and night. The young birds develop quickly and soon learn to cling and crawl. Hatched naked and blind, they begin to show feathers in less than six days, but their eyes do not open for two weeks. But sight really is not necessary in the dark chimney. For another week or so, until they are ready to leave, they cling to the bricks below the nest.

The chimney swift spends its life scouring the air for small insects. It would seem as though its tiny, short flat bill could not be effectively used as a fly trap, but when its mouth is opened wide, it extends back under the eyes. It is similar to the mouth of the whip-poor-will or nighthawk, but lacks the long bristles that help keep large insects from getting away.

By the middle of August many families of swifts have joined together. Late in the month great flocks are again roosting together and returning night after night to the same chimney. Almost all the swifts leave at once, late in September, and then only an occasional bird is seen. By the first of November the last ones have left the Gulf Coast and the United States. Where they went was a mystery until 1943 when 13 swifts wearing birdbands placed on them in various parts of the country were killed by Indians in the western Amazon Basin of eastern Peru. The chimney swift winters largely, if not wholly, in the tropical forests of the great Amazon Basin of South America. Thus one of the greatest of ornithological mysteries was finally solved through birdbanding (See under Bird: Birdbanding). Some superstitious people claimed that swifts buried themselves in the mud until spring. Others, however, for many years had suspected that they probably wintered in tropical South America feeding high over the jungle during the day, coming down only at dusk to roost in the hollows of forest trees.

Western North America has three species of swifts beyond the range of the

*The chimney swift builds a nest that is often attached to the inside of a chimney.*
*They also utilize caves, tree hollows, barns, and abandoned structures*

chimney swift that rarely reaches Montana and Wyoming. All of them are similar in habits and form to the eastern bird.

The white-throated swift, *Aeronautes saxatalis*, has white underparts marked with a deep black V. It usually inhabits the mountains, from southern Canada to Mexico.

Vaux's swift, *Chaetura vauxi*, is a more coastal species. It is dark and almost tail-less, like the chimney swift, and, is the smallest swift in North America, measuring about 4½ inches.

The largest is the rare black swift, *Cypseloides niger*, that measures 7¼ inches. It has a full, slightly forked tail and a small amount of white on the face. Its distribution is erratic, and it is seldom common in any of its widespread breeding area from Alaska and Canada through Mexico.     —A.B., Jr.

## SYCAMORE

**Other Common Names**—American plane tree, buttonwood, buttonball
**Scientific Name**—*Platanus occidentalis* ·
**Family**—Platanaceae (plane tree family)
**Range**—Southern Maine west to southern Iowa, and south to central Texas and northern Florida. Two other species with deeply cut leaves occur along streams in New Mexico and Arizona, *Platanus wrighti*, and in California, *Platanus racemosa*
**Habitat**—Bottomlands and stream margins, often planted as a street tree
**Leaves**—3 to 5-lobed, wider than long, and up to 12 inches across. The two types shown represent extremes of variation. The petiole (stem) is rather short and its conical base completely covers the following year's bud
**Bark**—Clear white, greenish or cream when newly peeled on upper parts of the tree, with patches of olive and tan farther down, finally flaky brown on the lower trunk. Curled pieces of peeled bark are found beneath the tree
**Flower**—Inconspicuous, appearing with the leaves in midspring

**Fruit**—A round ball of seeds 1 to 1½ inches in diameter, hanging on a cord-like stem

Introduced species of plane trees (a group to which our sycamore belongs) are more familiar about cities and towns, than the native species that is apt to be seen in the country in moist, rich soils, particularly along watercourses. During the winter their white upper trunks and branches stand out in sharp contrast to the brown woodland scene and make these trees easy to identify. The European plane trees and their various hybirds that are planted so often as street trees have smooth portions of the bark of a dull yellowish or olive-green color, quite different from the native species, and there are minor differences in the leaves. These trees are remarkably tolerant of soot and automobile fumes and add so much to the appearance of a city street that the virtue of such plantings could hardly be better advertized, especially in well-kept residential areas, informal business districts, and small towns.

No other native American trees have a bark development quite like the sycamore. On twigs it is greenish or tan but as the tree grows and the branches and trunks get larger the smooth bark weathers and flakes off in irregular oval areas exposing a creamy white or pale green surface, the whole assuming a vari-colored piebald appearance and only the main trunk and largest branches of older trees have a rough gray-brown surface.

This general sequence is true of all three of the North American species of the eastern sycamore, and of the two western species, all of which have leaves resembling those of sweetgum in shape and multiple fruits, or seedballs.

Sycamore wood is of medium to heavy weight and it is very tough and hard to split. It is frequently used for butchers' blocks, crates, boxes, some furniture and, formerly, for stereopticans, and barber poles.

Sycamores 175 feet or more with trunk diameters up to 14 feet have been measured, making this the largest deciduous species in the United States, but this comparative rating is further justified by the average size of the trees, which in some areas may be close to 120 feet tall with trunks 4 to 5 feet thick at shoulder height. This size, the bark colors, and the debris of bark peelings and very large leaves that usually collect at the foot of these trees make them recognizable at hardly more than glance.

The california sycamore, *Platanus racemosa*, and the Arizona sycamore, *Platanus wrightii*, are considered to be varieties within a species by some authorities, and two distinct species by others. Both have three or four fruits on each stem, instead of one as in the sycamore of the East. London plane trees and Oriental sycamores are often used as street plantings in cities. As with the western sycamores, the leaves are deeply lobed and several seed balls grow on each stem. —M.H.B.

## SYMBIOSIS

A relationship between two radically different organisms that benefits both of them is called symbiosis. In the strict meaning of the term, the relationship involves one of the partners actually living inside the tissues of the other, for example, as green algae in some of the protozoans, coelenterates, sponges, mollusks, and luminous bacteria in special cells of certain deep-water fishes.

Symbiosis is of widespread occurrence. The intestines of termites are infested with protozoans that break down the woody tissues eaten by the insect, into digestible food. Other insects may have fungi living within the body of the host. Plants of some families, especially the legumes, have nodules inhabited by bacteria that extract nitrogen from the air within the soil.

*Sycamore*

Some authorities use a more embracing definition for symbiosis, to include all forms of permanent associations between different species. *Parasitism* (*see Parasite*), where only one partner benefits and at the direct expense of the other, and *commensalism*, where one benefits and the other is unharmed, are called variations of symbiosis, and the relationship whereby both profit is called *mutualism* (*See also Joshua Tree; and Lichen*). —G.B.S.

Termites, aided by specialized protozoans that live symbiotically in their intestines, are the only animals able to utilize the cellulose of plants as food

T

### TADPOLE
*How the Tadpole Got Its Name*

Many brief summaries of medieval thought imply that no one in the period made careful observations of nature. It is true that a great many myths flourished. Numerous learned men believed, for example, that worms and other creatures were "spontaneously generated" from nonliving matter.

In spite of such fallacies, some rather incredible facts were firmly established. Take the early stage in the metamorphosis of the young of frogs and toads. Few other transformations are more rapid or so dramatic. Only rather painstaking study could have shown that the wee, wiggling creature absorbs its gills and tail in changing to a toad or a frog.

Detailed accounts are lacking. Yet language clearly indicates that the cycle of change was widely known before the 15th Century. For the tiny fellow that seemed all head and tail, with no outward resemblance to a frog, took its name from *tadde* (toad) plus *poll* (head). Centuries of usage have brought no change. The immature aquatic form of both toads and frogs still has the familiar name of *tadpole* (*See also under Amphibian*).                —W.B.G.

### TAMARACK (*See under Larch*)

## TANAGER

Four species of tanagers inhabit temperate North America. They belong to a group of birds that are characterized by short conical bills and rather long pointed or rounded wings that are marked with black, yellow, white, or red bands. Male tanagers (except for the western tanager) are more or less red in color during the summer and greenish dabbled with red in winter. Female tanagers are olive-green above and yellow below, but their wing markings are identical to the male's. Immature tanagers differ from the adults in that they have streaked plumage on their underparts.

The scarlet tanager, *Piranga olivacea*, is bright scarlet in summer and has black wings and tail feathers. This striking bird is common in eastern woodlands during the summer months.

The male summer tanager, *Piranga rubra*, is a rosy red bird that is not as brilliant in color as the scarlet tanager and does not have as strikingly contrasting black markings on its wings. Its range is generally a southern one, from southeastern California across the United States to the Gulf Coast and southern Florida and north to Iowa, Illinois, Indiana, and Ohio.

The mountains of Arizona, New Mexico, and western Texas are the home of the hepatic tanager, *Piranga flava*. The male is very similar to the summer tanager, a little duller in color, and can be easily identified by its blackish bill. All other tanagers have light bills. The female hepatic tanager is yellow and green and also has the black bill of the male. This bird prefers mountain woodlands and is usually seen near the tops of trees.

The male western tanager, *Piranga ludoviciana*, differs from other tanagers in color. The head of this species is red like other tanagers but it has a yellow breast and rump. Its back is black as are its wings that are lined with white.
—G.B.S.

**Scarlet Tanager**
**Other Common Names** — Black-winged redbird, firebird
**Scientific Name** — *Piranga olivacea*
**Family** — Thraupidae (tanagers)
**Order** — Passeriformes
**Size** — 6½-7½ inches
**Range** — Breeds from southern Manitoba, central Ontairo, southern Quebec, and Nova Scotia south to Oklahoma, northern Arkansas, central Alabama, and in the mountains to South Carolina and northern Georgia. Winters in Colombia, Ecuador, Bolivia, and Peru

The scarlet tanager is one of a large family of tropical species that has helped give the New World a reputation for brilliantly colored birds. It is bright scarlet, with black wings and a black tail. Of all the gaily-colored birds to reach the United States, the scarlet tanager is the greatest traveler. Some individuals reach Nova Scotia and southern Quebec.

Most of the brightly colored birds inhabiting the United States are not rare—in fact, they are quite common. This is true of the scarlet tanager, too. The reason the scarlet tanager is not seen as often as the Baltimore oriole is that it is a bird of the woodlands rather than suburban yards. In spite of its intense red color, it is not easy to see among the leafy crowns of the trees, where it spends most of its time.

The song of the scarlet tanager has been described as sounding "like a robin with a sore throat." In June it can be heard throughout the day, from short songs at dawn through the heat of midday when many other birds are silent. When not singing, the tanager has another note, a low *chip-purr* or *chip-bang*. Because the males can be located by their song, and because they are brightly colored, they are more easily recognized than their drab mates. The females are a dull green with yellow-green breasts that blend into the foliage perfectly.

*The male scarlet tanager is a brilliant bird of deep woodland treetops*

*Scarlet tanagers from Audubon's* Elephant Folio

The scarlet tanager has been called "the guardian of the oaks." In May, when these venerable trees are festooned with their brown-colored blossoms, the tanager can be seen eating small green worms that riddle the tender new leaves. Although oak woods seem to be a favorite habitat in the northern part of its range, the tanager can also be seen among pines and other evergreens. It is especially partial to woodlands where there is a mixture of beech trees and hemlocks. It arrives at its nesting grounds at the same time as the warblers, late in April or early in May.

The nest is rather shallow and flimsy, placed anywhere from 7 to 40 feet up on a horizontal limb. It is usually near an opening in the woodlands, especially where there are oaks, but it is sometimes situated in orchards, too.

The three to five eggs are a light green-blue marked with dark spots. The female broods them for nearly two weeks. The young birds, when ready to leave the nest, are green-yellow with brown wings, brown tails, and some brown streaks on the underparts. They are fed a great many insects when they are still in the nest, but when they leave they follow their parents to a wild cherry or mulberry tree if there is one in the neighborhood. Wild fruits do not have much food value, so a great quantity must be eaten. Insects are more substantial, and the scarlet tanager prefers gypsy moths, weevils, leaf-eating beetles, and all sorts of insect larvae.

In September the scarlet tanagers start moving southward, traveling at night with the great hordes of warblers. Leaving the North American continent entirely behind them, they are soon in the tropical jungles of northern South America where they join the colorful nonmigratory species of their family. By this time there is not even a touch of red in the males. They have changed into their winter plumage and can scarcely be told from the females except for their blacker wings.         —A.B., Jr.

**Summer Tanager**
**Other Common Names**—Summer redbird, bee bird
**Scientific Name**—*Piranga rubra*
**Family**—Thraupidae (tanagers)
**Order**—Passeriformes
**Size**—Length, 7 to 7½ inches
**Range**—Nests from southeastern California through southern Nevada to central Arizona, New Mexico, Texas,

*The summer tanager eats many destructive insects and their larvae*

*Western tanager, male (front); and female*

Oklahoma, and southeastern Nebraska to Iowa, Illinois, Indiana, Ohio, West Virginia, Maryland, and Delaware, south to the Gulf Coast, southern Florida and into Mexico. Winters from southern Baja California south into Mexico, Central America, and South America

The summer tanager, or summer redbird, as it is sometimes called, is perhaps not quite so widely known as the scarlet tanager, since its range is more restricted. During its summer sojourn it is primarily a bird of the southern states, although ranging north to Maryland, the Ohio Valley, and to southern Kansas. This rose-red tanager, to a greater extent than its brilliant relative, prefers open woodlands and has a special liking for sparse pine woodlands interspersed with scrub oaks. It also frequents lawns and orchards and is somewhat less retiring than the scarlet tanager. Occasionally it comes to plowed fields, where it may be seen picking up grubs and other injurious insects. The food habits of this tanager render it among our most useful birds, as large numbers of insects which are detrimental to the interests of farmers and fruit-growers are consumed.

Its song bears a general resemblance to that of the scarlet tanager and by some is thought to be sweeter and more spontaneous. The nest is usually near the end of a horizontal limb, is of leaves and strips of bark and lined with finer materials. From three to four bluish-white, or greenish-white eggs, marked with cinnamon or olive-brown, are laid.

**Western Tanager**
**Other Common Name**—Louisiana tanager
**Scientific Name**—*Piranga ludoviciana*
**Family**—Thraupidae (tanagers)
**Order**—Passeriformes
**Size**—Length, 6¼ to 7 inches
**Range**—Nests from Alaska and northern British Columbia east to central Saskatchewan, south to southern Nevada, southwestern Utah, Arizona, New Mexico, western Texas, and to northern Baja California. Winters from southern Baja California south to Mexico and Central America

Why, out of the whole tanager tribe— a family of 400 tropical species— only 2 should be adventurous enough to travel each year to Canada, is one of the many mysteries of migration. One, the scarlet tanager, lives in the eastern states; the other, the western tanager, occupies the West. They draw an invisible "no trespass" line across the Great Plains. They are counterparts for sure, even singing their short husky phrases in a similar manner, but the scarlet tanager is more partial to oaks, whereas the western tanager would rather live near pines or firs (although it often lives in oaks, too).

The western tanager's call note is a doubled *prit-ik*, by which it may be identified even during migration, when it occurs widely in many habitats. The beauty of the male western tanager, scarcely equaled by any other western bird, can often be enjoyed at very close range about a mountain or forest camp, for they come readily to accept fruit or cheese.

*The tapir is a native of tropical Mexico, Central, and South America*

## TAPIR
**Baird's Tapir**
**Other Common Names**—None
**Scientific Name**—*Tapirus bairdii*
**Family**—Tapiridae (tapirs)
**Order**—Perissodactyla
**Size**—Body Length, 6¾ feet; height at shoulder, 2½ feet
**Range**—Southern Mexico, Central and South America

Tapirs are timid, harmless, browsing mammals of deep forests, staying near rivers and lakes. They feed at night and remain hidden during the day.

Although their legs are short for so large an animal, and their bodies are plump and stocky, tapirs can run at an impressive rate when danger threatens. The chief enemy of this species is the jaguar, a large tropical cat.

The tapir has a short flexible trunk formed by the upper lip and the nose. Its main function appears to be picking leaves and buds from shrubs.

New World tapirs are dark brown as adults, spotted and striped when young. A related animal, the Malayan tapir, lives in Southeast Asia; it is black, with a wide white band about its midsection.
—G.B.S.

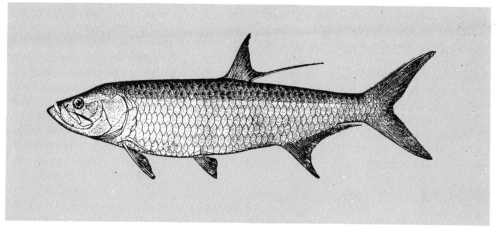

*Tarpons may weight as much as 350 pounds and live mainly along the Gulf Coast*

## TARANTULA
**Other Common Names** — Bird spider
**Scientific Name** — *Eurypelma steindach-neri*
**Family** — Aviculariidae (typical bird spiders)
**Order** — Arachnida
**Size** — Length, to 2 inches
**Range** — Southwestern United States

There are five closely related spiders of the genus *Eurypelma* in the southwestern deserts, all of them very much alike. Only *E. steindachneri* has a light-colored abdomen with a large velvety brown spot.

All of the tarantulas have hairy legs and bodies and are capable of moving swiftly over the sands to pounce upon large beetles that are their chief food. They are nocturnal, hiding by day in natural crevices in rocks and debris. The nest is lined with silk, but tarantulas do not spin webs.

Tropical tarantulas sometimes measure 10 inches across the outstretched legs and are known to prey upon large insects and even small birds.

The appearance of these large spiders, together with exaggerated stories of the potency of their venom, have given them a bad name. They are not known to be dangerous to humans and do not attack. European species, in medieval times,

were supposed to have a bite that caused dancing mania, compelling the victim to dance until the effects of the poison wore off. This belief has not been substantiated by the results of modern medical investigations.

Trapdoor spiders are closely related to the tarantulas. These dig burrows and cap the opening with a door of silk and debris. They also are nocturnal *(See under Spider).*                    — G.B.S.

## TARPON
**Atlantic Tarpon**
**Other Common Names** — Tarpon, silver king
**Scientific Name** — *Megalops atlantica*
**Family** — Elopidae (tarpons)
**Order** — Clupeiformes
**Size** — Length, up to slightly over 8 feet; weight, about 250 pounds
**Range** — Found mostly in the Gulf of Mexico, the West Indies, and off the coasts of Florida. Commonly in waters from Argentina to Brazil. Stragglers have been caught off the Atlantic Coast as far north as Cape Cod and Nova Scotia

The most striking physical feature of the Atlantic tarpon is its dorsal fin. The last ray of this fin is extremely lengthy and extends back like a long barb. This ray is often two or more times the length or height of the rest of the dorsal fin.

The fish is silver in color and its large, gleaming scales (larger than a silver dollar) are used by some natives as ornaments.

Although it has little commerical value as food, the fish is one of the most sought after of all game fish.

There are two other tarpons in waters off the coasts of North America. They are the machete, *Elops affinis,* and the ladyfish, *Elops saurus.*

**TAXONOMY** (*See Classification of Plants and Animals*)

**TERMITE**
**Other Common Names**—Common termite
**Scientific Name**—*Reticulitermes flavipes*
**Family**—Rhinotermitidae (termites)
**Order**—Isoptera
**Size**—Length, about one-fourth inch
**Range**—Eastern and southeastern United States west to central Texas

Termites are, at first glance, antlike insects; however, they differ from the true ants in several important features. Perhaps the most important of these differences is the way in which the termite's abdomen is jointed to the thorax. Unlike the members of the order Hymenoptera (ants, bees, and wasps) that have a very conspicuous constriction at the waist, the termites are thick-waisted creatures. Their soft bodies are equipped with a pair of short *cerci* on the last abdominal segment, and they have two pairs of wings that are almost equal in length—a feature that at once places them in the order Isoptera (*Iso,* equal; *ptera,* wing). The ants, bees, and wasps also have two pairs of wings, but the hind wings are shorter than the forewings.

Only in the swarming sexual forms of termites is any appreciable amount of pigment present.

Although morphological differences separate the termites from the ants, wasps, and bees, they are very similar to them in that they are truly social insects—the only example of sociality outside of the order Hymenoptera. In general, a termite colony is divided into four distinct castes. The first, the kings and queens, are sometimes seen in early summer when they appear in swarming masses. During their brief mating flight, the kings and queens pair off. After the mating flight, which may carry the new founders of termite colonies some distance from their original homes, the wings are shed and the females begin laying enormous quantities of eggs. These develop into three distinct forms that become the other castes. The second, and largest caste, consists of the workers. These large, colorless, soft-bodied insects lack eyes and are responsible for building or enlarging the colony and for tending to the queen. A third caste of similar creatures is in charge of defending the colony against intruders. These soldiers are equipped with fierce-looking mandibles on their large heads. The fourth caste consists of an emergency reproductive form that can take over egg production in the case of death of the original reproductive pair. The third and fourth castes are sometimes differentiated in form within the caste. For example, some soldiers may have long "noselike" parts replacing the mandibles, and a subdivision of the emergency reproductive caste might entirely lack the wing buds that are present in the typical form.

Termites usually live beneath the soil and construct a passageway of soil and debris to connect their colonies with a source of food. Their diet consists of the cellulose of wood—a substance that is, for all practical purposes, undigestable by other living things. The digestive process is accomplished by the presence of a one-celled animal, or protozoa, that lives in the alimentary tract of the termite.

It is estimated that termites do some 40 million dollars worth of damage annually to wooden structures, fence posts, telephone poles, and other items. Eighty percent of this damage is in the South. Repellants have been developed for use on railroad ties, fence posts, and other wooden items that are in contact with the soil. The basic principle in termite control is to break the link between the subterranean burrows and the source of food. This can be achieved by mechanical barriers, soil poisons, and structural changes. —G.A.B.

### Birds—A Natural Check on Termites

Termites are a tremendous "biological success," yet there are times when they are eliminated locally in a remarkably short time.

A well-known American naturalist came upon a swarm of winged termites on a Baltimore city lawn one day where a robin was devouring the little insects just as fast as it could. Its manner seemed so eager and the insects so inexhaustible that the naturalist stopped to watch. There were several hundred termites massed on less than a square foot of ground. They were crawling over and up the grass blades.

The robin ate eagerly for five minutes, then gathered a billful of the termites and took them across the street to a rose arbor in which it had a nest with four downy young. Then it came back again and resumed its own gorging. Meanwhile, apparently attracted by the robin's activity, a starling came and fed briefly, then two house sparrows, a second starling, a third house sparrow, and finally, a chipping sparrow. For another five minutes these birds worked on the termites. And though the swarm must for a while have been replenished from underground almost as fast as it was decimated, when the last bird—it was the robin—had departed not a termite remained.

Hundreds of termites had been eaten. But that was not all that had happened. Hundreds more—thousands—indeed, hundreds of thousands—had been prevented from being born. Termites are

hideaway creatures; most of them spend their entire lives underground, or inside the wood upon which they feed. Only one purpose ever brings into the open, at one or two periods of the year, the winged members of the colony—which develop only at these times. That purpose is the making of a flight that will result in the establishment of new colonies (*See also under Ant*).

The winged termite swarms contain both males and females, and the flights these make are sometimes called nuptial flights. They are not really that; the termites do not conjugate in the air, as ants, butterflies, dragonflies, and some other insects do. They merely fly about briefly, for distances varying with the species. With *Reticulitermes flavipes*, the ones the naturalist had been watching, the distance is sometimes only a few feet—then they come again to the ground. Upon alighting, their wings fall off or are rubbed off. Individuals of opposite sexes that meet each other then begin associating by twos, and these pairs dig into the earth. In those new burrows, some days later, conjugation finally begins and the new colonies are launched.

Some authorities say there are 10 species of the genus *Reticulitermes* in America. *R. flavipes* has the widest distribution in the eastern and southwestern United States; *R. tibialis* appears to be spread over the widest area in the central and south-central states; *R. hesperus* occurs largely along the Pacific slope from British Columbia south into lower California.

On another occasion, the naturalist noticed the feeding of birds on termites that were attempting a flight. This time the insects were merely straggling up at intervals from between the bark and wood of a low stump. There was no safety in small numbers, however. Inconspicuous as this swarm was, a white-throated sparrow repeatedly, over a period of two hours, went to the stump

*Termite*

and picked it clean. A flicker also did that, and did more; it thrust its long tongue down under the loose bark in quest of prey that had not yet come into the open.

Perhaps no creature on earth is unqualifiedly "bad." Even the termite is not; away from man it is decidedly "good." It is one of the agencies that help to decompose the highly resistant cellulose of dead wood. "The termite problem arises," Charles A. Kofoid, an authority on the insect, has written, "because of man's attempts to change the ordinary processes of nature by preserving for his own use, over considerable periods of time, wood and its products, which it has been the immemorial function of the termites and associated organisms to break down and return to the soil and the atmosphere."

So, too, with the English, or house, sparrow. Highly objectionable to some people in many ways, this bird nonetheless does economic good, as by its habitual attacks upon termites. These are habitual; they were recorded from Maryland and New York in the famous study of the house sparrow's food published by W. B. Barrows of the United States Biological Survey in 1889. Bringing that study up to date in 1940, E. R. Kalmbach of the United States Fish and Wildlife Service, both widened the area and emphasized the economic value of the house sparrow's feeding activities.

The presence of termites in "considerable numbers" in stomachs from Alabama, he wrote, "corroborates field observations that the house sparrow is an energetic destroyer of these insects when opportunity presents itself."

Of course, the native birds that the house sparrow often displaces are also great termite destroyers. Termites seem, indeed, to be wonderful delicacies to any form of insect eater; they are sought not only by birds, but by some other insects, by lizards, and even by some primitive races of men. A robin once demonstrated to what lengths a bird will go to get them. A man undertook to burn away an old stump on his grounds, and as it burned a colony of termites began leaving it. While the stump still smoldered the robin flew on it and feasted on the insects.

And for those termites that escape terrestrial dangers and get launched upon their flights, on the wing they are eagerly devoured by the aerial feeders among the birds. During an investigation he was making into the economic value of birds, S. D. Judd, a federal government food habits investigator, noted that a swarm of *Reticulitermes flavipes*—it is the most widespread eastern species— had got into the air and "fully 200 swallows, mainly bank swallows, with a few barn swallows and tree swallows, were very busy among them." Seven of the swallows were shot, and were found to have eaten, altogether, 320 of the termites.

Nighthawks, swifts, and several kinds of flycatchers are other aerial-feeding birds known to destroy termites, and the full roster of the avian eaters of termites runs to at least 40 species. The creatures that feed on all termites are so numerous and sharp-eyed that the entomologist Leland O. Howard has written of *Reticulitermes flavipes* that its dispersal flight "always, except when it occurs in houses, attracts birds and other insect-eating creatures so that most of the individuals are destroyed."—H. B.